Riordan

ESEA i

ARCHBISHOP RIORDAN HIGH SCHOOL

7269
Animals as social beings   591.5 POR

S0-BEW-519

ANIMALS AS SOCIAL BEINGS

ANIMALS
AS SOCIAL BEINGS

ADOLF PORTMANN

*Professor of Zoology at the University of Basle
and Director of the Zoological Institute*

Translated from the German by
OLIVER COBURN

New York   THE VIKING PRESS   1961

SAN FRANCISCO UNIFIED SCHOOL DISTRICT

Published in 1961
by The Viking Press, Inc.
625 Madison Avenue, New York 22, N. Y.

Library of Congress Catalog Card Number:
61-11425

★

Das Tier als Soziales Wesen
Copyright 1953
by Rhein-Verlag AG., Zurich

Animals as Social Beings
Copyright © 1961
by Hutchinson & Co. (Publishers) Ltd.

591.5
P837

ESEA
1967 68

Printed in the U.S.A.
by The Murray Printing Company

Contents

Photographs

Line Drawings

Preface

This book makes no attempt to present a comprehensive survey of social life in the animal kingdom, and it has comparatively little to say of the best known and most striking societies, like the amazing insect colonies, which have been dealt with very thoroughly in many excellent studies. In the following chapters I shall be concerned primarily with the basic phenomena of this 'social life', and shall try to show to what a large extent all higher forms of animal life are in fact social. In analysing and illustrating the significance of the social element for the species on the one hand and the individual on the other, I shall be well served by the methods and results of modern 'behaviour research', one of the most recent branches of biology. I make no claim to be comprehensive, of course, nor to present the findings in strict historical sequence; also, my personal experience and inclinations will naturally play a big part in the examples chosen. For the development of the new 'social research' in the last few decades is something I myself have lived through, while my own scientific work has kept me variously and continuously in touch with it.

As an extension to this primary subject I have found it necessary to describe the great changes which have occurred in the concept of the organism, and the relation of such changes to developments in philosophy and psychology, so as to bring out the less obvious connections between these branches of knowledge and the whole of natural science.

I should like to express my gratitude here to Frau Olga Froebe-Kapteyn and her colleagues of the 'Eranos Congresses', at which since 1946 I have tried to present the results of biological work in their more general significance. The encouragement and stimulation I always derived from these congresses have contributed greatly to the appearance of this book in its present form. I am also extremely grateful to my publisher, Dr. D. Brody, and

9

to his assistant, Herr Bucher, who have shown so much patience and understanding in the book's production.

My thanks are due to Frau Trudi Homburger-Schriever, to Mr. Eric Hosking (London), to Dr. Jean Sapin-Jaloustre (Paris), Herr Hans Traber (Heerbrugg), Herr Emil Weitnauer (Oltingen) and Herr Dietrich Wittmer (Basle), who have very kindly made available to me their valuable photographs; and to the following publishing houses, societies and magazine proprietors who have given permission for photographs from their books or periodicals to be reproduced: E. F. Brill, Leiden; F.-Enke-Verlag, Stuttgart; A.-Kernen-Verlag, Stuttgart; Innes Publishing Company, Philadelphia; New York Zoological Society; the *Illustrated London News*, the *National Geographical Magazine*, *Natural History*, *Life*, and *Audubon Magazine*. Finally, I would express my very warm appreciation to Fräulein Sabine Baur, who has taken great care over adapting several of the diagrams for the purpose of this book.

My presentation of the fundamentals of social life is also meant as part of a wider whole, clarifying our ideas of the organism, as I have tried to do in my other writings. I hope this book may succeed in showing the many ways in which the secret realm of animal 'psychology' is being explored; and I shall be very pleased if the extensive quotations from the reports of research workers help the reader to feel a direct participation in the latest biological developments.

Adolf Portmann.

1

The World of the Dragonflies

ON A BRIGHT June morning we stand in the dappled shade of some bushes by a river bank, and let our gaze shift from the bustling river to quieter corners of the bank. The sunrays will reveal there a teeming life, which includes the rainbow glint of the dragonflies: with dark blue wings, bluey-green stick-like bodies, bluey-green bullet eyes in a broad head, they flit swiftly around, to settle here and there along the bank. If we watch them for a while, thinking of them as creatures living their own life (where human beings are at best disturbers of the peace), then with luck and patience we may witness things we could never have guessed at, and be transported into a strange, mysterious new world.

Before long we shall discover other dragonflies of the same species, with amber wings and hind-quarters more yellow than green; closer observation will show that they are the females, while the blue-winged ones are males. This species, *Calopteryx virgo* ('maid with beautiful wings'), has also been named (by Linné) the dragonfly of running waters; and there is another species living in Switzerland, called *Calopteryx splendens*, whose males have a 'navy blue' stripe on each white transparent wing. The females of both species look more green than blue, and the wings are always transparent: in *splendens* the softest shade of green, in *virgo* rather more smoke-grey and under sunlight slightly amber. In the areas where I have watched them *virgo* is the commoner, and in the last thirty years I have spent many a summer day studying these dark blue and amber insect-couples.

But since then a great deal of hard work has been done, bringing many new methods and results, and the description which follows is derived particularly from the results of the

11

detailed studies published in 1951 by Christiane Buchholtz. *Calopteryx virgo* develops in the water as a rapacious grey-brown larva for about two years, but once it has turned into a dragonfly proper (in this final stage it is called an imago) its span of life is rarely more than twelve days. The whole business of reproduction is carried out in these few days, which are crammed with activity and are extremely important for the continuing existence of the species. Let us now have a closer look at the imago's activity, which has been established by biologists after countless hours and days of field-work over the years. It is indeed significant of the new phase in biology that animals are studied not only at moments when something particularly exciting is going on, but in their 'routine' every-day life (Plate 1).

The dragonfly day begins about nine o'clock. The male, who is first to emerge from the rigidity of sleep, will look for a good 'territory'. This is a small reserve, usually about four yards in diameter, from which each male hunts his prey and also attacks rival males flying past—in defence of his chosen territory. But he only keeps it for a day; the next morning he will find a new one.

When the sun climbs higher, the females too start flying. They have no territories, and stray far further from the water in their hunt for smaller insects. With their golden wings and glinting bodies, they are often to be found in sunlit clearings, on a look-out from which they can start hunting. If one of the females flies into a male's territory, and both are 'in the mood', mating may take place, a really remarkable phenomenon. And it can be observed not in some remote tropical land, where we readily imagine such scenes, but right at hand in our own countryside.

Close study of the larger dragonflies reveals a sexual distinguishing mark at their posterior end: the female has two small appendages, and at certain times a leaf-shaped sting underneath for sticking her eggs in plants; whereas the male has a sort of trident with its two side points lying above. The middle point (sometimes made up of two separate ones) lies below, and with the two above forms a strong pincers. Figure 1 shows this mating

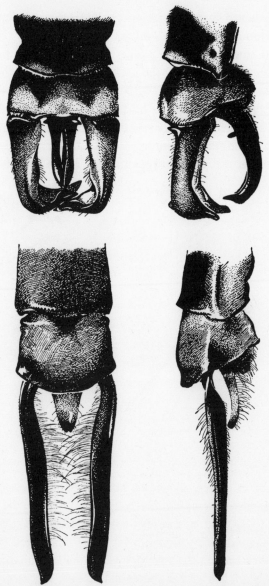

FIG. 1. The mating organs at the end of the male dragonfly's body are differently formed from species to species. Above, those of *Onychogomphus forcipatus*, a European species; below of *Plathycantha acuta*, a species from New Guinea. (Left, seen from above; right, from the side.)

apparatus, which varies characteristically from species to species, and is very important in the study of dragonflies.

After a courting flight the blue-winged male uses his trident pincers to grip his mate by the neck, the front of the thorax and back of the head. The pair sit on a plant and take up a peculiar position: first the male bends his body into a circle, a movement the purpose of which is only revealed by careful anatomic study. He has an organ for transmitting sperm; and very curiously, this is not found at the actual sexual aperture in his hindquarters (in

FIG. 2. The mating of *Calopteryx splendens* (after C. Buchholtz, 1951).

the ninth of its eleven segments), but in front in the second and third segment. By making his body into a circle, he fills the sperm reservoir, and he can only copulate after this preliminary. The pair sometimes fly around a bit in a four-winged 'tandem', though never leaving the territory of the male, who now drives his mate's head, held in his abdominal pincers, repeatedly against the sperm reservoir. Finally they come to the actual copulation, forming the mysterious 'mating wheel' (Figure 2), which is unique in the whole wide field of insect life. I wonder how often natural scientists in olden times were struck by it; as far as I know, it was first described by the Strasbourg fisherman, Leonhard Baldner, in his book on birds and fishes written about 1666.

The gripped female thrusts her hindquarters forward, her sexual aperture comes into contact with the male's reservoir, and the sperm flows into the female's genitals. The pair stay in this wheel position about a minute and a half on average (Plates 2 and 4).

Then release comes, but the female stays in the territory, and the male takes an obvious 'interest' in her actions. She climbs down the stalk of a plant to water level, and begins to insert her eggs into the soft part of the plant. Her hindquarters grope under water for a good place in the fabric of the plant to stick her egg in. She is so absorbed by this task that she climbs right into the water and sinks the eggs up to sixteen inches below the surface.

Christiane Buchholtz' careful observations show that with *Calopteryx splendens* the females always insert their eggs above the water in some stretches of a stream and below in others. Perhaps there are groups among which each of these practices may be fixed by heredity; here we meet the possibility that a new way of life may be established within a single species. While studying this characteristic of *Calopteryx*, Frau Buchholtz witnessed an instance of the male insect's interest in what the female was doing—which illustrates the extent of differentiation possible in these dragonflies' behaviour:—

'At one *splendens* habitat the females regularly laid their eggs under water. Suddenly one of them after copulation unexpectedly stuck her eggs into the plant *above* the water. The male obviously noticed this, for he immediately "made a correction": like lightning he dived under water before her eyes, and then came straight out again. The female thereupon at once disappeared under water and acted as was the custom here. The males are therefore also capable of certain co-ordinated movements, which are normally only executed by the female when laying eggs.'

We should of course be on our guard against too anthropomorphic an interpretation, the suggestion that the male was
'showing' the female what to do. As Frau Buchholtz remarks,
the male may have latent potentialities for performing female
actions; his dive may have stimulated the female to follow suit.
To understand how such a 'social' stimulation can work unconsciously, we need only remember how liable we are ourselves to
such imitative action: how infectious, for instance, is a yawn!
The only conclusion I would draw from this striking scene among
the reeds is that the dragonfly's actions in the reproduction period
may include very complicated impulses and rests on a subtle
inter-action with a mate. Let us follow the life of these insects a
stage farther, so as to observe some other species besides the
Calopteryx in the stranger phases of their existence.

                    *   *   *

The scene is a reedy pond, on a day in early summer. Dragonfly pairs, deep blue and needle fine (belonging to the genus of
Agrionids, a world-wide genus with very many species), are flying
to and fro, and here and there a pair settles on a reed for mating,
in the 'wheel form' we have already seen with *Calopteryx*. The
novelty here, however, occurs after the climb down to the water.
The pairs sit on drifting bits of reed; you may see one just settling
after the mating is completed. Often there are several lined up
on a stalk one behind the other. The male insect (we know he is
the one in front) stands straight upright, very stiff, his wings
quivering, the pincers at his rear anchored to his mate's head
and the front of her thorax. His state of excitement would be
manifest even if we knew nothing of the feeling by which he is
gripped (Plate 3). He is stimulating the laying of eggs—for that
is the act we are watching. With this particular species (*Platyc-
nemis pennipes*) the act is always carried out in couples, in contrast
to *Calopteryx*, where the female does it alone. With other
species there are differences as between different regions: the
same species (*Ischnura elegans*) lays alone in Switzerland, but
in couples in Denmark. It would be fascinating to see these

Plate 1. Male (above) and female (below) of *Calopteryx virgo*. The female's wings have a bright 'wing-mark' (absent from the male's), which is more pronounced with other dragonflies. It is there called 'Pterostigma', here 'pseudopterostigma'. *Photos: Dietrich Widmer.*

Plate 2. Mating of a species of *Agrion,* usually completed at rest.
Photo: Dietrich Widmer.

Plate 3. An *Agrion* pair laying eggs. The rod-like insect is the male. The female inserts the eggs into a leaf under water in regular succession.

Photo: Dietrich Widmer.

Plate 4. Dragonfly wedding — the mating wheel of an *Agrion* pair. The male is a very light blue, the female more greenish.

Photo: Trudi Homburger-Schriever.

differences marked on a map of Europe, if only we knew what they were over the whole wide area. When pairs lay eggs together, they sometimes enter the water together, if (as with *Erythromma najas*) it is under water that the female lays her eggs.

C. Wesenberg-Lund (1913), one of Denmark's great natural scientists, describes the scene at a pond full of yellow water lilies:—'The lilies cleared the water by about three inches; pairs of egg-laying *Erythromma*, females accompanied by males, were found sitting between the flowers and the water, often five or six arched pairs on the same stem. The laying of eggs starts a little under the flower. Slowly, with every egg deposited in the stem, the female moves a bit downwards. The curve of her abdomen flattens. The sting is inserted again and a new egg planted. The whole thing lasts only a few seconds.

'If the female cannot reach any further with her abdomen, she climbs further down, accompanied by the male. Often she sinks the eggs in neat zigzag lines. When she reaches the surface of the water with the point of her abdomen, she goes on climbing down till she eventually disappears under the water. The wings beat upwards and are often held under water in this position owing to the air clinging to them. The male, his pincers still firmly grasping the female's thorax, also moves into the water, drawn by her. Soon they are both under the surface. They can be seen through the water as silvery gleaming garlands drifting slowly downwards, the female laying eggs all the while. The stems of the water lilies are about five feet; but as soon as the female has reached a depth of four inches, she stops her egg-laying. Then the two insects can be seen to free themselves. A coat of air brings them swiftly and safely upwards. I have seen five pairs at a stem under the water at the same time. Twenty-five minutes is the longest time I have observed them under water. The male often emerges rather sooner than the female. The result of *Erythromma's* egg-laying is a gall of the entire lily stem. The whole surface, covered with the eggs (which are yellow at first), gets a spongy appearance, and the stem grows thicker.' (Figure 3.)

In late summer and autumn almost any pond or marsh offers us a further variant of this egg-laying: these pairs are dragonflies of the genus *Sympetrum*, in which the males have a reddish body (scarlet in *Sympetrum·sanguineum*) and the females are rather less conspicuous, a brownish colour.

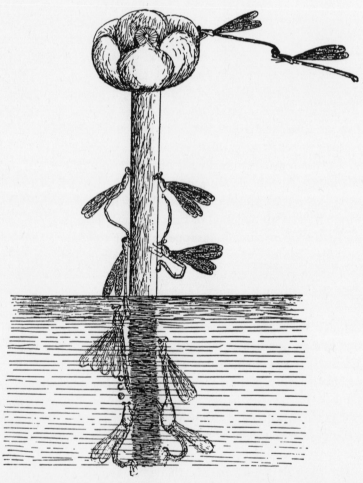

FIG. 3. Pairs of dragonfly (*Erythromma najas*) laying eggs on a yellow water-lily blossom. The pair on the right under water have a shining silvery pocket of air round them, on the left a pair are just separating and climbing out of the water (after C. Wesenberg-Lund, 1913).

The mating-'tandem' in this genus is very striking. Whereas with their cousins, the Libellulids, the union is broken off after successful mating, *Sympetrum* is unique among dragonfly genera in that the couples remain united after mating, a four-winged creature of the air, to perform the next act in the reproduction drama, the laying of eggs, above water. Over thirty years ago, when I was studying this phenomenon, I formed the impression that the male was the leading partner, determining the pair's graceful gliding up and down, during which the female drops a few eggs into the water every time she descends. Very recently the male's leading role has been confirmed by Moore in England (1952): he succeeded in getting a male of *Sympetrum striolatum*, who was flying at large, to catch a dead female moved on a thread and fly a 'tandem' with it. The strange pair were led by the male in typical sinking movements, till the end of the dead female's hindquarters touched the water. The females of this genus sometimes lay eggs alone as well; but normally the process is a combined action guided by the male partner. The interest displayed by the *Calopteryx* male in the egg-laying female in his territory must surely be regarded as a first step in the sequence of evolutionary processes leading to the pair's complicated egg-laying rites.

When a *Sympetrum* 'tandem' is laying eggs and a single male happens to fly near, he is stimulated by the pair's behaviour into climbing and sinking in time with them, stopping when they stop and starting again when they resume work. We meet the expressions of an induced state of excitement. How strong this excitement is in the female can be seen from the following: to obtain eggs for my own 'farm', I often caught a 'tandem' pair, freed the female, held her by the wings, and in rhythm with a pair's flight dipped the end of her body in and out of a jar of water I had prepared. Every time she touched the water, she laid some eggs—real testimony for the strength of the drive, considering how badly her normal functioning had been disturbed.

That *Sympetrum* is the dominant genus of dragonfly in many

countries, may be due to several factors; but one such factor must be the advantages gained by this genus from the egg-laying in pairs (increased excitement and greater persistence, choice of the laying place by the 'freer' male, perhaps even avoidance of enemies). The female's drive can be directed on the egg-laying more intensively if the male is in charge and free to keep a look-out. An extreme form of this common egg-laying is reached in an American species of the genus *Tramea*, whose behaviour is described by Kennedy (1917) as follows:—

'Usually every female had a very attentive male companion. As *Tramea* seldom alights, the male would catch the female on the wing. While holding her the pair would fly about over the surface of the pond, stopping occasionally to oviposit over the surface where this was free from the scum of algae and duckweed. The pair would poise about six inches above the water. The male would release the female and remain poised, while she would drop to the surface, and with a short swing, tap the surface just once, when she would rise to the male, who would instantly grasp her thorax with his claspers, without first seizing her with his feet. This quick release and the almost immediate reclasping of the female was one of the most dexterous performances I have ever observed in dragonflies.'

How powerful the drive to such 'tandem' formations can be is shown by an observation Moore reported in 1952. He saw a chain of three dragon-flies: in a typical *Sympetrum* tandem another male had harnessed himself to the first male, gripping it by the head and front of the chest—so as to satisfy his urge towards 'combined flying'.

*   *   *

Our glimpse into the world of the dragonflies poses a row of general questions which touch some of the essentials of social life.

First, there is the question of 'recognition': how do creatures of the same species find and recognise each other? We have seen how exactly a *Calopteryx* male, lurking in his territory, will distinguish a rival male or a female to be courted. The sensory capacities, the marks of the species, the means by which mixing the species is avoided—all this belongs to the fundamental problems of social research.

Nobody who has seen the big bullet eyes will be surprised that sight is the most important among these aids to social life. Few insects show eyes of such a size, made up of many thousand facets. With some species of big dragonfly, the insect's whole front is a large seeing-apparatus formed out of the two half-bullets of the eyes, a complicated structure of visual nerves connected to the brain. This optical apparatus directs the dragonfly's whole orientation.

The importance of the visual functions for orientation has, of course, been known for several decades. The motions of the dragonfly's head with his pair of eyes are controlled from the thorax in such a way that when he is at rest his visual field can remain motionless. This is not so obvious as it may sound, for he often settles on leaves and branches moved by the wind. Every passive movement he makes, every inclination left or right forwards or backwards, is so equalised by automatic turning o the head that he has a clear horizon in front of him remaining relatively the same, offering a background for the moving objects which interest him: insects to feed on, rivals, mates, enemies (Uexküll, 1921). For observation also shows that it is the optical marks which enable the watchful male in his territory to reach an understanding with his selected female and which altogether determine his orientation (Plate 5).

The proof of this demands experiment, that is to say observation under conditions arranged by the scientist himself and aiming at the answering of a particular question. When it comes to experimenting with dragonflies at large, the difficulties are considerable. The biggest species and the most rewarding for observation are either excellent or at least very fair fliers, so that they cannot be kept in a modest glass case: they need space for their activities. But to make exact judgments on these activities when they are at large, it must be possible to recognise the individual again. Colour-marking might be used, but many dragonflies are harmed by being caught for marking, because their flying apparatus is very subtle and delicate. Spraying with colour is an alternative which Moore, for instance, has used for identification purposes: while resting on a twig, the insect is sprayed with a few drops of permanent adhesive colouring; note is made of where the spots happen to come on the transparent wing of the individual insects, which can thereafter be easily identified.

Biologists are also increasingly making a novel use of anglers' methods in observing dragonflies; and although anglers may smile a little, it has produced good results for biology.

There are two such methods. The first, which requires some skill, is to put a fine loop round the bodies of bigger dragonflies in such a way that they can still fly freely but can be fetched back by the observer, and more especially can be directed within certain limits or stopped in areas where interesting encounters are possible. The dragonfly is obliging enough to fly whenever its legs feel no firm grip; this automatic flying makes it a good deal easier to carry out such angling experiments with our intrepid fliers.

The second method is to juggle something in front of the lurking insect. Their reactions to this, with careful interpretation, can yield many conclusions on their sensory potentialities and on how things present themselves to the dragonfly.

So far as I can see, these angling methods were first practised with dragonflies by St. Quentin (1934). Later N. Tinbergen used them for studying butterflies; Christiane Buchholtz experimented on *Calopteryx* in this manner, and Moore found a fishing-rod handy for tackling a whole series of questions. It was a simple idea, but as ever, somebody had to think of it first! Back in 1923 Tirala floated tissue paper and threw little paper pellets to test the dragonflies' seeing of shapes—a much more laborious and uncertain business than the 'angling'. He did, however, discover that where the object is not too big, it is the speed with which it flies or floats, and not its shape, which is effective as initial stimulus.

The experiments with *Calopteryx* (Buchholtz) have shown that the mating ceremonies could be evoked by a few characteristics of the mate: whether the male insect had a whole dead female, a pair of wings or only a single wing juggled before him, he always reacted by gripping it, providing that the 'bait' moved, showed the right wing colour of the female, and above all, had the transparency of real wings. When pieces were stuck together to simulate a bigger wing, or when a wing was made smaller, a positive reaction was produced with wings between $\frac{4}{5}''$ by $\frac{7}{20}''$ and $1\frac{1}{2}''$ by $\frac{4}{5}''$. The normal wing of a female measures $\frac{3}{10}''$ by $\frac{2}{5}''$, so the effective bait was somewhere round this average size. Subtle differences of shape, however, had no appreciable effect on the experiment.

It is above all the size of the dark-blue field which produces the reaction typical of the species. Thus the females of *Calopteryx splendens* always choose only the smaller blue field characteristic of the males of their species, while those of *virgo* probably react only to the larger blue field characteristic of the males of theirs (though the question has not been tested experimentally with species other than *splendens*). From these angling experiments carried out with dragonfly wings as bait, the most important 'catch' is the conclusion that behaviour typical of the species is innate in these insects when they turn into imagines, having emerged from the water as larvae, and having never seen a full-grown dragonfly before.

All the unknown processes in their central nervous system are thereby set in motion, ensuring the effects of optical forms just revealed; each sex enters the last phase of its life with a 'knowledge' in which certain essential features determine a 'picture' of the mate. This 'knowledge about the mate' varies in both sexes from species to species. Thus a male will sometimes pursue the female of another species, but she will always reject such advances. The 'picture' of the male in her mind must be rather more precise than that of the female in his—which of course corresponds to the fact that the males are more conspicuous to human eyes as well.

We enter here the world of innate (inherited) behaviour patterns. It is a vast chapter, and what we know about it today from dragonflies alone is so many-sided that for the moment we can only give it a passing glimpse.

The experiments on how dragonflies meet each other introduce a second problem of social life, for human beings as well as the rest of the animal kingdom: that of inner condition or mood. When a female dragonfly flies into the territory of a waiting male of the same species, copulation is not simply the certain and as it were automatic consequence. One female may 'run away' from the male's courting flight, while another female who comes along, just as much by chance, will fall in with it. Chance happenings may also put a waiting male, who seemed just ready for pairing, into a quite different mood in which he misses good opportunities. We have already come across the stimulating role played by the sight of other members of the species. Observations on *Calopteryx* show that after their emergence from the larva, the imagines form sexual elements in a few days. Colouring at the same time reaches its full development, and the behaviour processes of reproduction set in.

The momentary mood is dammed up, as it were, by long waiting, so that for instance a male who has waited in his territory a long time without a female flying in responds to the decoys with the greatest readiness; whereas the repetition of such stimulation to mating leads to a swift reduction in the readiness to respond. In his normal every-day life the *Calopteryx* male after successful copulation maintains his interest in his egg-laying mate as long as she is doing her laying in his reserve; even if other females fly in, a new copulation never takes place during this time.

Moore's experiments also dealt with mood, and he showed with dragonflies of the genus *Aeschna* that at an 'artificial' encounter (presentation of one partner on the hook) two males meeting do not always clash as rivals, but a futile tandem-flight sometimes takes place—even, in very rare and exceptional cases, between males of different species. But *Aeschna* is a very different genus from *Calopteryx*; mating mistakes occur much more rarely with the latter.

*   *   *

In the summer months of 1918 to 1920, when I was following up the life of *Calopteryx*, no one showed any close interest in the adult male's possession of a 'territory', a more or less extended area of river-bank; but in recent years the significance of this has been increasingly realised, and made the subject of special investigations.

It was a factor which did not come out first in research on dragonflies, but in quite a different field, the study of birds. Aristotle and Pliny mention the claim by birds to particular territories, but scarcely any attention was given to this; nor was there much more when Altum made the point in 1868. It did not really register with biologists till the British ornithologist, E. Howard (since 1907, but above all in 1920) expounded a theory that brooding birds possessed a territory for the purpose of preserving the species—and thus showed it to be a definite evolutionary factor.

The theory of the territory has undergone several substantial changes, and it is differently interpreted today by different biologists. But the decisive point is that a compact mass of single facts were gradually recognised as forming a whole new picture which included the concept of purpose. The realisation that research into causes and into purpose is complementary, represents one of the biggest advances in biology since the twenties.

With Howard's theory research on this new concept took a big step forward, and we shall note its most important features because they have proved extremely fruitful. The assurance of a definite territory, usually round the nest, is of great importance for birds in preserving the species, because it decides the

SAN FRANCISCO UNIFIED SCHOOL DISTRICT

distribution of members of the species over a large area, and thereby increases the possibility for many couples to be formed. It also increases the ties of the pair on each other and thus contributes positively to the rearing of young; and to some extent provides a private food store both for the couple and their young.

As has been said, details were modified: the first simple theory put forward has been replaced by a series of important ideas concerning the species-preserving value of many phenomena of social life among animals: these ideas have fertilised scientific discussion, have led to new experiments and an amazing extension of our factual knowledge. The realisation that territory is a biological fact has helped to obtain full attention for the subjective spheres of owning and defending it, and has made the most subjective thing of all, the individual's experience and social impulses, a field for new objective research.

Since then special impetus has gone into defining the territory of reptiles and fishes, and thoroughly analysing in all its aspects this factor of territory-owning. Finally, the biologist investigating the life of dragonflies, for instance, has been faced in the last decade by an entirely transformed scientific climate: realising the importance of territories, he can follow with new eyes the distribution of *Calopteryx* along a stream, of *Aeschna* at the edge of a pond, or of *Gomphus* by the banks of Swiss lakes. He discovers here, so far from all vertebrate structures, something like territories, and thereby confirms once again that these insects must be ranked quite high among animal forms. He discovers also that social structures of this sort extend beyond the confines of the different systematic groups. Admittedly, dragonflies look for a new territory every day, whereas vertebrates own and defend one for a relatively long period; but the one-day territory may still be one of the simplest forms of 'possession of space'.

Of course there are many different kinds of dragonflies, representing as many different evolutionary trends, and Moore's observations of the large genus *Aeschna* (one of the *Anisoptera*) make it probable that their battles, rustling encounters and wild wrestling bouts in the air are based far more on the mating urge than on defence of a territory. It looks as if with many of the bigger genera such clashes were caused by a failure to distinguish between the sexes. I do not think, however, that this excludes the male's possession of a territory. The distribution along part of a bank is often strikingly regular, especially when there are more than enough favourable haunts to go round. This suggests at least a temporary lordship over a domain.

Calopteryx defends his territory with far greater vigour, and among Swiss dragonflies this genus shows the most conspicuous difference between the sexes. The male, therefore, avoids the confusions made by *Aeschna*, and can doubtless distinguish rivals from potential mates far more exactly at a distance. In this respect the two genera are at opposite extremes, and we can expect many shades of difference in between them.

Let us now look at one of Moore's reports, which is concerned particularly with *Aeschna* and *Anax*, the largest of our dragonfly genera: 'On several occasions the effect of a new arrival at the stream has been observed. On these occasions violent clashes are almost inevitably observed. In some cases both insects remain by the water, but the beats of the original insects are altered or shortened. If the newly arrived insect leaves the water for a short time, the original insects resume their original beats. In these cases the size and position of the beat of each dragonfly is in part, at any rate, determined by those of other insects. On other occasions after the initial clashes one of the insects has been observed to leave the water. It appears that during the course of the day there is competition for space along the stream, and that once a certain approximate density is reached, it is not exceeded . . . Presumably learning is involved: it has been observed on several occasions that the insects concerned tended to avoid the site of the encounters.' (Plate 6.)

These innocent summer scenes take the thoughtful biologist far away from the pond and the water-lilies. His mind turns to all the attempts which have been made to consider the organism as a machine; and we become aware that this remote insect world, which lived on our earth 250 to 300 million years before birds and mammals, yet leads us right into the midst of the problem of psychology. Scientists today are discussing the role of 'learning' and true 'intelligence' among insects and other invertebrates. This is not a temporary regression to outmoded anthropomorphic ideas, but an advance in knowledge building on a deepened analysis of the life of these forms. The scientist today has achieved a new grasp of the animal organism.

Remote as the dragonfly world is from our own, the behaviour of these insects testifies to an internal structure—which allows several different shades of expression. It will leave us less astonished that biologists today should find such fantastic correspondences between very different forms, should come on similarities between birds and fishes, for instance, and often have good reason for comparing insects and birds. Our sojourn among the dragonflies brings us an insight which we shall be meeting again and again, like a *Leitmotif* in music: the hint of a mysterious something in insects which can almost be called mood.

One more general factor is thrown into relief by the behaviour of the dragonflies; and this too must be considered, if we are to grasp the new ideas of the organism now quietly coming into their own under the influence of modern biology.

There are over a million separate species of insects, according to zoologists' estimates; and for our present purpose it would not matter if there were only 750,000. The overwhelming majority of them use the features characteristic of the insect body for the business of preserving their species: the genital apertures and the mating organs coordinated with them (which in fact are greatly transformed limbs) are situated at the eighth and ninth segments of the insect's abdomen. Yet in this tiny group of dragonflies, which has existed since the palaeozoic age, a completely new and exceptional way of mating has somehow been 'worked out'.

Of course the phrase 'worked out', though in line with evolutionary thought, raises many difficulties. How has the special behaviour of dragonflies 'developed' from the original arrangement of mating organs and mating behaviour characteristic of all insects? Before such a development is complete, there are so many stages to pass through, and even the preliminaries are formidable enough. A new sperm reservoir must be produced in the male, requiring an additional movement to fill it; the pincers must be formed and the actions necessarily bound up with them; this means that the central nervous systems of both sexes must be correspondingly modified, without which the pincers would be useless . . . and so on. Not that I am trying to argue against evolution! It is only a reminder that we are still a very long way from being able to explain how the great natural phenomena first came about.

But the dragonflies have something important to show us in this respect. According to the evolutionary view of nature the typical method of reproduction among insects has a certain purposefulness, being a positive factor in preserving the species; but here a method with the same purpose, which has long proved its efficacy and is still employed by all the dragonfly's relatives, is given up by a group in favour of a complication which, to say the least, goes beyond the bounds of that necessity so readily brought up in interpreting natural phenomena. That *today* the dragonflies' preservation of the species depends on the strict fulfilment of all the complications, the gripping of the female, the filling of the sperm reservoir, the copulation wheel, etc.—is not in doubt. For the success of this complex operation every limb is necessary, but it has not yet been proved that the whole operation itself was 'necessary' in the first place. In other words, a new system has been established, but we cannot say that *it had to be* established just because a structure has come into being which is now an indispensable part of the system.

* * *

To a superficial glance these dragonflies would scarcely seem to be 'social' insects. It is all the more important to show that the social element is a basic fact among these insects which are so readily called 'solitary'. There is the recognition of other members of the species, the richly differentiated partnership of the sexes, the distribution of available space among potentially rival males; all details we shall meet as important factors in actual social life. This first look into a strange world—right in the midst of our own—has thus been a useful preliminary to the questions of how, and how far, animals live together.

A *Calopteryx* male waits in his small territory. Is he waiting *for*, expecting something? Who knows? But we do know that within him there is something which has prepared him for encounters with females and rival males he has never seen and for the way he will behave at such encounters. In other words, a dragonfly has the innate ability to react to certain situations of which he has no previous experience. When we observe the life of these insects with our full interest, it is as if we could hear all the instruments tuning up for the concert of social life among animals. Now we are ready for the overture.

2

The Change in Methods and Aims

To SEE THE changes which have occurred in the field of behaviour research, I shall take a problem which has wide significance for social life and leads to the most general biological questions: the behaviour of the digger-wasp *Ammophila*. Excellent studies of it have been made at an interval of over half a century, by J. H. Fabre in *Souvenirs Entomologiques* (1880) and G. P. Baerends (1941); and a comparison of these works, both remarkable in their own way, will bring out the special qualities of research methods in our own day.

J. H. Fabre (1823-1915) carried out his great life's work in sunny Provence. At that time there was a tendency to overrate laboratory research, but Fabre justifiably believed that studying insects 'in the field' would yield far more, and more accurate, evidence as to their way of life than could be hoped for in an artificial environment where the insects were completely isolated and disorientated. Called by Darwin himself 'the incomparable observer', Fabre remained a lonely figure, not only because of his declared opposition to Darwinism—which he saw at the height of its offensive and its political applications—but because such loneliness fitted in with his whole personality.

He was a political dissenter, who made so much of a cult of doing his own documentation that he may hardly have been aware of others' discoveries, especially those of his contemporaries. Isolated as he was, he had little chance to refer to the latest books and journals; but attempts to dramatise Fabre's life as that of a great neglected genius leave out of account the recluse's pride and indifference to public judgment. He is rather the great solitary whose whole make-up is fundamentally opposed to many present-day attitudes; to understand him, one

31

must appreciate not only an exceptional scientist, but also the particular circumstances of the times he was living in. If certain scenes from insect life have come to the forefront of biological investigation—such as our problem of the digger-wasp—homage is due, though often not paid, to the great hermit genius of Sérignan at the foot of Mount Ventoux.

Permeated by the idea of an unchanging unity of form and behaviour in individual species, Fabre's laborious investigations, extending over most of his life, give a magnificent description of the special characteristics of individual species and families. But of his many-sided life's work his studies of the digger-wasp have received especial attention, and I shall confine myself to comparing his work on the *Ammophila* genus with later studies of it. All the different stinging digger-wasps prey on other insects or larvae, sometimes even spiders; they sting one of these insects several times to paralyse it, carry the captured prey into breeding holes they have dug themselves and lay an egg on it. The wasp larva, a legless maggot which emerges from this egg, thus finds its food waiting, just as the larvae of certain solitary wild bees have been supplied with honey by their mother while they are still in the breeding comb. At first sight the digger-wasps might seem solitary, non-gregarious insects, but we shall meet peculiar features of social life among them (Plate 7).

Fabre's work was devoted to careful investigations of the hunting methods of the different species—locust-killers, spider-hunters, beetle-collectors and caterpillar-catchers—each strictly limited to its destined prey. He also examined the tactics, varying from species to species, by which they paralysed their victims; and he showed important structural differences in the use of the sting by the various species relating to the character of their victims. For these wasps seem to operate as if they were quite familiar with their victims' anatomy. Finally he examined closely the building and enclosure of the breeding holes and many other details of this remarkable behaviour.

After observing a great many individual insects in the field, often a very laborious process, and sometimes supplementing the observations with others made in his insectarium, he reached a 'natural history' of the various species, establishing in the case of our digger-wasps that they keep to inherited ways of behaviour with remarkable rigidity. Until his day the species were classified in a rather monolithic system by a mere roll-call of different names with no individual life in them. Fabre was determined to make the description of a species something far more animated, and readers of the *Souvenirs Entomologiques* must agree that he triumphantly succeeded in this aim.

We are so remote from that past age, of course, that we can scarcely appreciate any more the intellectual background against which Fabre's work shone out as something great and revolutionary; and in the light of modern research methods we see far more clearly his stubbornness, prejudices and inadequacy. He achieved so fully his most important aim, to make the whole life and behaviour of a species into the subject of special research, that today his own work is a matter of history. But his wonderful descriptions can still arouse our admiration despite all the amendments made necessary by later studies. In judging Fabre's work, we should also remember that the present methods of the laboratory were developed only in his later life. University scientists who consider the founding years of our Institutes must be struck by the recentness of present-day working methods and all that these include even in school science.

Fabre did, it is true, have the great tool of the new age, biological experiment, very much to hand; in fact he pioneered its use. But he never knew anything about another essential side, the organisation of science by the perfection of its instruments. For the new form of research is identifiable by whether or not it can be assimilated to the work of an institute. The wide range of tasks to be undertaken puts the accent increasingly on group work, less and less on the achievements of the individual. However indispensable these may be, the face of research in our time is determined by the established institutions, which have the technical means, the funds and the libraries at their disposal and within whose framework alone the essential work of our time can be carried out. That such a state of affairs has its dangers and may impede true creative research, is no doubt true, but another story.

Fabre certainly cannot be imagined within this framework, either as head of a laboratory or as a professor in the lecture-room. His work must be seen as something complete in itself, comprehensive and individual. If he did not fit in too easily with the scientists of his own age, that may enhance the contrast between him and a scientist of today.

*   *   *

In the years just before the second world war, when the Dutch biologist G. P. Baerends was tackling the problem of the digger-wasps, the background to biological research was utterly different. He had no need to enlarge on the life picture of the species, and could plunge deeper into more particularised questions. The idea of transformation of the species, which Fabre had fought against so aggressively, was now accepted, even though there was still plenty of dispute about how the mysterious transformation took place. Baerends no longer had to devote his attention to the fixed and apparently unchangeable aspects of insect behaviour, but could concentrate on its more plastic sides. He could start from the certainty that Fabre's concept of instinct among insects was too rigid, and that the wasps' whole behaviour included some innate, fixed parts and some plastic parts, which could be distinguished by careful analysis. He also had to analyse instinct more precisely, and separate it into factors which often varied greatly in importance. Indeed a detailed study of the two men's different approaches to this one problem shows the whole change in the use of the word instinct.

Without going into the history of this change step by step, it should perhaps be mentioned that criticism of Fabre's concept had already begun at the turn of the century. The observations of S. W. and E. G. Peckham (1898 and 1900) and several other studies had demolished the idea that the sand-wasp's life moves in a fixed and unalterable way. And of course the methods of biologists had been transformed by them as well as the questions they were probing.

Naturally, therefore, Baerends' methods were very different from Fabre's in following up the wasp's life story. He observed the digger-wasps not over many long stretches in an extensive territory, but on a limited area of Dutch moorland, about a hundred yards of a sandy track where a great many wasps had their nests. He was studying not 'the sand-wasp' but all the individual insects in their particularity, whose behaviour would provide the norm for the species as well. A way of marking had to be found, and Frisch's experiments with bees formed a prototype: spots of colour in various places on the insect's thorax made a great many distinguishing marks possible, whereby a wasp's activities could be exactly followed over days and weeks, giving an insight unprecedented till then into a form of life so remote from our own. Baerends also wanted to find out more about the sand-nests of the individual wasps: to watch what happened inside these nests, he worked out a system of marking them with angled wires, the angles of which pointed exactly to the nest. Further, he invented an artificial nest of plaster-of-Paris, which in many cases he put under the wasp in place of its own— and which was almost always accepted. Through such artificial nests observers could have more frequent controls and could perform a variety of experiments impossible with a sand-nest (which would be damaged more easily).

Every morning, before the first wasps moved out of their nests, he was in position, on a folding chair about two yards from the nearest nests, with his binoculars, microscope and note-book. The sand-wasp's day begins before half-past seven, and ends at six in the evening, when the last wasp flies off to its sleeping-place on the heath. Baerends observed and noted ceaselessly, only now and then letting a trusted colleague take over. He studied altogether about 120 wasps in 400 nests, giving up July and August over five years to this intensive study of a tiny section of insect life: some 1,250 hours in all. This is but one illustration of the immense patience, loving care and scientific curiosity which are put into such studies (Figs. 4 to 6).

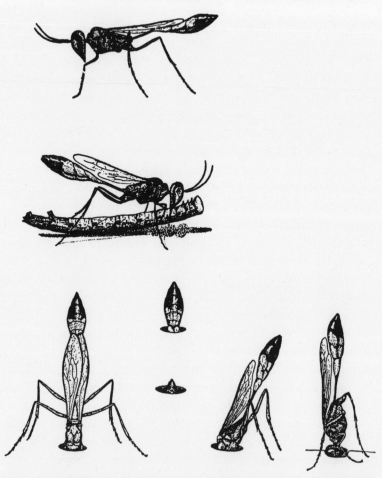

Fig. 4. Characteristic attitudes and movements of the female of *Ammophila adriaansei*. Above: dancing. Middle: with a caterpillar. Below, left: digging the nest-hole in the sand. Below, right: on closing the hole, the wasp presses the sand very hard with her head, and levels the area (after G. P. Baerends, 1941).

I cannot here give all the advances which we owe to Baerends'
work in this field; but a few of them must be mentioned to show
how they could have been achieved only in this way, and because
they illuminate important facts of social life among animals.

Observations at the beginning of the century had already
pointed to one sign of unexpected complexity: against the

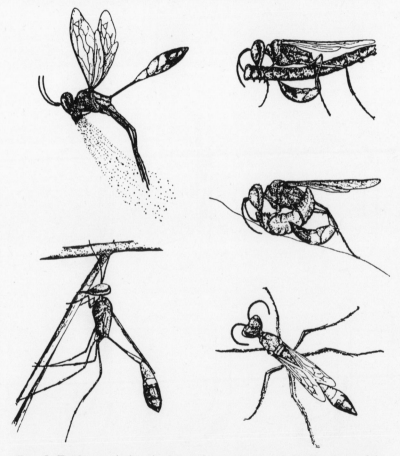

FIG. 5. Further typical attitudes and movements of female *Ammophila*.
Above, left: in flight she drops sand, which she has taken for nest-building.
Above, right: stinging a caterpillar. Middle, right: attempt to sting another
larva. Below, left: sleeping position on plants; right: sunning herself. She
often enjoys a sun-bathe in breaks from work (after G. P. Baerends, 1941).

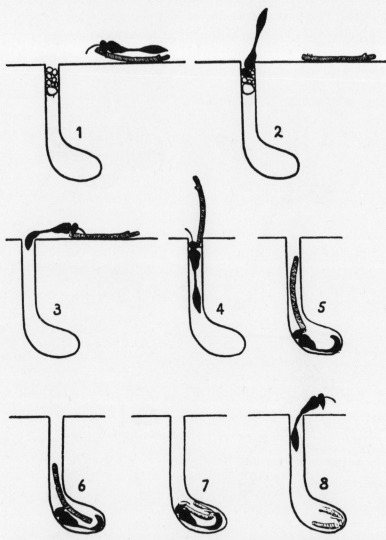

FIG. 6. Sequence of actions in an *Ammophila* nest up to egg-laying: (1) the caterpillar is put down, the nest being shut; (2) the nest is opened; (3, 4, 5, 6) the caterpillar is gripped and pulled into the hole; (7) a longish egg is laid on the caterpillar's body, after which the wasp leaves the nest (after G. P. Baerends, 1941).

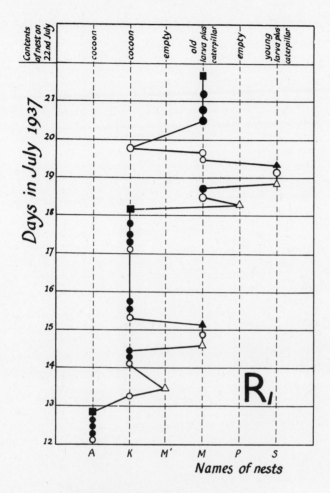

FIG. 7. Code: ○ Inspection visit (without caterpillar)
● Bringing in caterpillar
■ Final closing of nest
△ Digging nest
▲ Laying egg on caterpillar
(after G. P. Baerends, 1941).

Diagram of activity of wasp R_1 from 12th to 21st July, showing the purposeful co-ordination of work which enables the wasp to work on several nests (6 in this case) simultaneously. Nests A and K were already there before the observation period represented; A, K, and M were finally closed during this time; work on S continued.

assumption that each female wasp worked exclusively on a single nest at any given time, Baerends found that she worked on several nests at once. She visited the holes already supplied

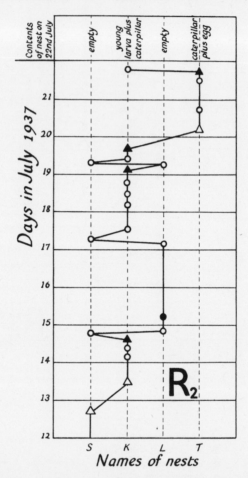

FIG. 8. Diagram of activity of wasp R_2 during the same time as R_1 was observed. Nest L was dug before observation period; it was found empty on two inspections and abandoned. In Nest S, dug on 12th July, despite various checking inspections, no prey was ever brought in, nor was an egg laid. In Nest K a new egg was laid three times on a new caterpillar whether because of the young larva's death or because of disturbances to the nest. This diagram when compared with that for R_1 shows how greatly differentiated individual behaviour is (after G. P. Baerends, 1941).

with food, without dragging anything in: these 'unladen visits' were simply inspections to show her how the hole was developing. If she found an egg in the nest, she would not bring another caterpillar there but started work in another nest. Later, sometimes several days later, she returned to the first nest. If she found a larva there which had emerged in the meantime, her next visits would be to bring it food, from one to three caterpillars for young larvae, from three to seven for older ones. But if the larvae in the nest had perished, the female wasp, while working on two to three other nests, returned several times before giving up the first (Figs. 7 and 8).

Again through knowledge of individual wasps the observer can reach conclusions about *Ammophila's* powers of memory. We can establish beyond doubt that one wasp, after working several days on different nests, returns to all the holes she has cared for before. Another, after six days work of various kinds on several nests, finds her way back to an old nest she has supplied before. In both cases they 'remember' whether the nest is temporary, i.e. needing later attention, or has been finally secured for the protection of the pupa.

Ammophila has strange 'dormitories': those of one small group Baerends found in such a moorland 'dormitory', up to thirteen on a single plant, less than four inches from each other· For his observations threw light not only on the insects' astonishing memory of places, but also on the habits of both individual and groups, for instance, the way members of one group gradually come to choose new sleeping places.

The Table on p. 42 shows clearly how true to one place individual insects remain (e.g. XXO, GXO). Some, after spending the night in a 'strange' place, return to their 'headquarters' or 'home' (XXR, GXX).

For many years Dutch research workers have been intensively studying *Ammophila campestris*, and by reporting local peculiarities have established that this species is particularly variable. In 1947 A. Adriaanse, following up Baerends' work, showed that

Table.   Visits to sleeping places in the course of several days.

Wasp	Sleeping place where wasp was found in evening										
AXX	b	–	c	b	e	–	b	c	–	–	c
XGX	e	a	–	–	c	c	a	c	–	a	e
GXX	c	b	–	c	c	c	b	c	–	–	–
XBX	–	a	d	–	–	–	d	d	–	–	–
XXG	a	b	b	b	b	–	b	c	–	c	–
XXO	c	–	c	c	c	c	c	c	c	c	–
XXR	d	d	d	d	d	–	c	d	–	d	–
XWX	c	c	c	c	c	–	–	–	–	–	–
GXO	–	a	a	a	a	a	a	a	–	–	a
Date: August 1940	16.	17.	22.	23.	24.	25.	26.	28.	29.	30.	31.

the commonest variant of the species in Holland—the form, therefore, which Baerends studied—was subtly distinguished in structure from the main species; it is, in fact, described now as *Ammophila adriaansei*. So far as we can survey the genus today this species alone has the habit of building in several nests at once; the typical *Ammophila campestris*, once it has started work on a nest, goes right on to the feeding of the larvae and the eventual closing of the nest. It also brings in saw-fly larvae, while the other type hunts caterpillars of the hawk-moth. The lucky chance that Holland is pre-eminently the home of the *adriaansei* type has made us familiar with a specially differentiated behaviour pattern, thereby enriching our ideas as to the potential complexities of sand-wasp life.

That life has thereby become unexpectedly a subject for social research. The digger-wasps were once thought of simply as 'solitary', whereas with these species most intensively studied we now know that they lead a simple kind of group existence. Although in their habitat there are plenty of nesting places favourable to a genuine solitary life, they seek out particular zones where they can build their nests in large groups. Within these 'compounds' they live in groups, which also look for common sleeping places, though of course in a very loose and flexible way. The 'lay-out' of the nests aims at keeping a certain distance from neighbouring nests—so a sort of 'territory' exists, which is specifically used by this one particular wasp, and within which the owner drives off and fights other members of her species.

The result of deeper analysis is the discovery of unexpected complexity and a great wealth of differentiated happenings. Like the once 'unsplittable' atom—and what a host of separate parts we have to take into account today!—the concept of instinct has also been split up into many parts. Earlier scientists thought of it as the mysterious unifying force of all living things, while today it is a complex with parts significant in themselves and so different that many behaviour research workers have come to find the common term 'instinct' a hindrance, and would like to eliminate it completely from the description of animal behaviour. In some aspects, admittedly, their methods fit in perfectly with J. H. Fabre's outlook, and here he must certainly be considered the great pioneer: for instance, he emphasised the need for describing animals' actions, he recognised that they must be studied in their natural sphere, and he rebelled against exclusive reliance on laboratory work and the attempt to study special facets of animal life by isolating the animal under controllable conditions. These facets of Fabre's approach remain essential still for the exact physiological study of the inner functional connections and individual sensory activities; but modern research workers have recognised that their experiments must be carried out under very different conditions.

* * *

The history of animal 'psychology's' development is full of pioneers who have not been recognised as such or had any successors for a decade or more. Many biologists today, for instance, would hardly believe that Julian Huxley's remarkable studies of the courting habits of the Crested Grebe were published as long ago as 1914. 'A good glass, a notebook, some patience, and a spare fortnight in the spring—with these I not only managed to discover many unknown facts about the Crested Grebe, but also had one of the pleasantest of holidays.' So Huxley wrote himself, and he was helping then to open up a new sphere of observation and a vast field for new theoretical experiments. The same hidden effectiveness can be claimed for the unobtrusive but striking studies by Jacob von Uexküll, the second edition of whose book *Umwelt und Innenwelt der Tiere* (Animals' Environment and Inner World) was published in 1921; and by O. Heinroth, the indefatigable observer of birds' behaviour. These and many other biological works have led to a transformation in methods to which we must pay careful attention if we are to understand biology's struggles and results in the field of social research.

The historian of this transformation must also be able to appreciate the significance of apparently trivial discoveries as they are gradually brought to completion. We take it for granted today that genuine study of a society is only possible if its members can be observed clearly and as individuals; but this essential condition has only been accepted very recently. Although, for instance, as early as 1899 Mortensen in Denmark introduced the systematic identification of birds by ringing their feet, it is only a few decades since this method has spread widely enough to be regarded as a scientific instrument, or with the marking of mammals to promise real results. In the remote oceanic world of whales this new method brings new certainties where till now we have had to rely on age-old mariners' yarns.

Anyone acquainted with naturalists and research workers who use such methods will know with what care and attention to creature habits they try to do the marking at the moment which is most favourable and in the way which is least disturbing. I stress the point because sentimentalists often make unjust criticisms of such marking, a technique which, sensibly applied, has had very fruitful results, as can be shown by a few examples.

From 1932 to 1943 H. Arn in Solothurn ringed a colony of Alpine swifts (*Micropus melba*), which was nesting in the roof of a baroque church (they are easily accessible in their nesting colonies). By the sure identification of individuals he discovered an amazing wealth of details, far above that general 'natural history of a species' with which we formerly had to be content.

This was how we first learnt something certain about the age an individual bird can achieve. Only the ring enables us to recognise that in many nests the same pair returns year after year, while in other nests one bird appears with different mates. One of the birds in Solothurn hatched in the same nest for twelve years, another for eleven; perseverance in a breeding place from four to six years has been proved quite common for individual swifts. Arn found the same pair in a nest for six years in succession. His results did not prove conclusively whether the lasting attachment of Alpine swift pairs to each other is due to the bond with their nesting place; but E. Weitnauer's observations on their smaller relatives, the wall-swifts, in Oltingen produced more concrete information on the matter. In 1942 a pair mated in the starling box of an orchard. Weitnauer did not replace the tumble-down box, and in the spring of 1943 saw the same pair stop at the old nesting place. They remained together and found new nesting possibilities in the church tower. The year after, they went back to the same nesting place. So their staying together was clearly a different tie from what had once been an individual tie with a nesting-place. Their fidelity to each other is the more amazing in that every year they went through the immense journey to and from their African winter quarters. Weitnauer also established by ringing that the wall-swifts had five-year 'marriages'.

Ringing gives information too on the attainment of sexual maturity in swifts, showing that they achieve reproduction in the second year of their lives, that is, in their second summer. The exceptions to this rule are also recognisable beyond dispute from ring numbers; the same applies to the life of the unmated birds in their first year, their roaming and their appearance in strange colonies, where they sometimes settle for good.

*　　　*　　　*

Let us now consider the work of N. Tinbergen on herring gulls (*Larus argentatus*), not so much at the moment for its results, as for its methods. In Holland's large gull colonies Tinbergen and his assistants examined the relation of the chicks to the old bird, especially their begging for food. As has been known since Friedrich Goethe's observations in 1937, this begging is stimulated by the sight of the parental bill: the bottom of the bill is bright yellow with a patch of striking red, which flashes particularly brightly in the sunlight that falls through the bill's transparent tip. It is not simply an ornament; as experiment shows, it forms a necessary link in the chain of factors which ensures the young gulls' nourishment and quick growth. It has also been shown by experiment that the response to the red patch is innate behaviour, that when the chick comes out of the egg, before it has ever seen a female gull, something in it is waiting for a red patch on the bill. But to prove this beyond doubt immense experimental work was needed. The behaviour of the chicks just out of the egg had to be tested (before they had had a chance to learn from experience); and as they learnt very quickly, Tinbergen soon found out that to examine a real state of '*naïveté*' he could only use them for a few hours. So he kept taking chicks just out of the egg from a large colony, showing them various models of bill in his tent, noting their reactions, and then after about six hours returning them to their nests, where at this early age they were at once accepted again by their parents without hesitation (such experiments were therefore no danger to the continuity of the species).

A gull chick which is hungry responds very promptly: in favourable cases about thirty times in thirty seconds when it is shown an effective model of the parental bill. To get a picture of the work involved in these experiments, I would mention that 16,000 responses of gull chicks were recorded and carefully worked over in answering twenty different complementary problems.

As another illustration of how intensive such fieldwork can

be, R. A. Hinde in England made a study of great tits between September 1948 and May 1950, which involved about 1,500 hours of observations in the field; to this must be added the results of the automatic recording in nests, as well as all the information given by fellow research workers. Over 130 tits, made recognisable as individuals by colour rings, were followed in their behaviour over the year. This also illustrates the team-work which is a special feature of today's scientific methods, in striking contrast to J. H. Fabre's deliberate isolation.

Even in captivity, where smaller fauna are studied in aquaria and insectaria, it is important to produce conditions similar to those the creature would meet at large. Far-sighted observers sometimes express doubts as to whether even favourable conditions may be regarded as a true picture of those found in nature. Happily, such doubts as far as zoos were concerned, gave a powerful impulse to the building of open zoos. The influence of behaviour research, as well as a new feeling for nature, has thus brought about a transformation in ways of keeping animals, turning the forcing ground of the menagerie into a great natural reserve. Hediger's important work, *Wild Animals in Captivity*, is a weighty document of this transformation and also a valuable instrument in pressing it further. Essential results for behaviour research have been confirmed in zoos, while on the other hand there is hardly an important discovery about the social life of animals which has not also been of great significance for their keeping and breeding.

For instance, the new insight into the role of territories and habit-formation has helped to dispose of an old prejudice which led to the commonest criticism of keeping animals in a zoo. The observation of animal societies out of captivity has put paid to the idea of wild animals roaming at large, at least in the case of many species. We know today that many groups of mammals will have enough free movement in a limited space. These insights have also shown the importance of particular places in the animal's living space where it can feel secure. Altogether they have given magnificent inspiration to the building of zoos with special regard for the animal's rights as well as for the demands of visitors and observers. How much a zoo may become a *home* for many groups of animals, is illustrated by a remarkable case in the Munich Zoo at Hellabrunn reported by Paul Eipper for 1943-4, the year when Munich had its heaviest air-raids.

'One night the blast of a mine destroyed most of the wire fences and many of the wooden animal houses and feeding sheds. To all intents and purposes all the big game long "locked up" in the fenced enclosure were now free—if still alive. No one was surprised that before the final all-clear the herd of Asiatic buffalo had disappeared. "Thank God there's no mangled or burnt buffalo lying about," said the zoo director. "Give the herd a little time to come to rest. For *their* understanding, last night was a specially bad tropical storm. They've probably gone into cover down by the water meadows. They'll come back of their own accord." Four o'clock in the afternoon—the feeding time they had been used to for years! With the old leader cow at their head, the great Indian buffaloes moved up from the bushy river bank, trampled over the fallen fence back into their "prison", and stood waiting for their food outside the rubble of the sleeping and feeding sheds—even the huge, dangerous, strong-horned bull. Quite as a matter of course the keeper appeared with his food-barrow. While the animals ate, the zoo staff put up the fence again and mended it for the time being. It did not need to be very strong anyhow, that fence; it was only a symbol of protection, not a prison wall.' Similar incidents from the war years have been reported by other observers.

It is to be hoped that zoos will become an increasingly important feature of our towns, giving us contact with all the wide-ranging forms of animal life which the world can offer. Equally important is the 'natural' keeping of animals, even on the most sober practical grounds. For it is only with good keeping that a group of animals can attain the special mood which makes normal reproduction possible. To breed animals yourself instead of

Plate 5. One of the bigger dragonflies (and better fliers) — *Libellula quadri-maculata* — lurks for prey. The large eyes register every movement within the visual field; the tense body is ready to pounce. Dragonflies often return when flying to the same 'look-out'.   *Photo: H. Traber.*

Plate 6. *Aeschna cyanea* is one of the biggest species of European dragon-fly. The huge eyes touch each other on the centre line and form one of the most powerful optical apparatuses in the insect world. Unlike *Calopteryx* and *Agrion* species, which fold their wings when at rest, the big forms keep theirs spread even then. *Photo: H. Traber.*

Plate 7. An *Ammophila* female has caught a big caterpillar. She stings the victim's nervous system (lower picture). It may be seen thereby that the slim 'wasp waist' is an important aid in reaching the underparts of the caterpillar with the sting. Above: with immense effort the huge prey is dragged to the opening of the nest. *Photos: Dietrich Widmer.*

Plate 8. Gathering of knots *(Calidris canutus),* a shore-bird the size of a thrush. Top left: two oyster-catchers. This tight-packed gathering makes a striking contrast with the ranks of the oyster-catchers in Plate 9. There are some 10,000 birds here. *Photo: Eric Hosking.*

capturing them in the wild is something that must appeal for·
practical reasons as well as from the point of view of animal
protection, not to mention the delight which young and old
everywhere can find in watching young animals.

Good keeping, ensuring of the animal's right disposition—
how they are to be achieved the animal keeper can discover only
through many-sided and deepened knowledge. In the widest
sense, therefore, social research has also become a prerequisite
of our animal-keeping, just as zoos are always making new con-
tributions to social research.

*   *   *

For scientists today, investigating social life among animals,
the use of experiment is obviously vital; and animal biology has
this advantage over human biology that more 'controls' are
possible by means of experiment—also with fewer ethical questions involved. For we are all aware that technical and scientific
advances, unaccompanied by an advance in morality, present a
grave danger to the human race. All scientific experiment has to
guard against contributing to this result, but biology must also
take into account the rights of the living creatures being experimented on, the limits to which experiment may go. These rights,
these limits, become increasingly important the higher the
organism, and the nearer our own, which is made the subject of
experiment and may be decisively changed by it. So although
experimentation in human biology is fraught with these ethical
difficulties, animal biology has them also, even though to a lesser
extent, and they must never be ignored.

Experiment allows conclusions to be reached which would
otherwise be impossible. In the realm of behaviour research I
need only mention that the really decisive proof of innate forms
of behaviour in the animal can be achieved only by experiment
(apart from a few lucky experimental situations devised by nature
itself), whereas with man a scientific decision on this problem is
more or less impossible in very important cases. The basis for
conclusions on innate forms of human behaviour is very narrow

and fragmentary, and many of the things we do know about man
go back to the result of experiment on animals.

In my view, however, what gives biological work its greatest
importance in forming our picture of nature and man, is its
ceaseless contact with the mighty realm we know of in human
behaviour as 'the unconscious': in this respect biology has a
significance for the whole life of our time which is still too little
recognised. Of course a human being can never be considered
purely as a 'biological fact', and I recognise that the message of
every science is only partial. Nevertheless, by carefully bringing
out single aspects of biological research, I shall try to fit them into
a general picture which is the sum total of all methods of research
open to us.

3
Forms of Social Life

WE ARE FAMILIAR in every-day speech with a great many different types of animal collective: flocks and herds, shoals of fish, flights of birds, swarms or hives of bees. Biologists can only consider these as forms of society where the group's existence is dependent on a distinct relationship between the individuals in it. In other cases it will be more 'sub-social' life than social. For instance, although the mother sand-wasp of the genus *Ammophila* is continuously and intensively occupied with feeding her young, the larvae, though dependent on her for food, are scarcely aware of her and have no real relation with her. Still, her activity on their behalf and her 'memory' of 'arrangements' for the completed nest are important isolated parts of a potential 'social' complex.

We also meet this potential in a group of insects called Bethylides, which are rather like ants in appearance. In the exotic forms of the genus *Scleroderma*, the females attack beetle larvae much bigger than themselves in rotten wood. So do the digger-wasps, but their tactics show an amazing precision, whereas *Scleroderma* does not always overcome her prey. If she does, she feeds on the juices of the captured (and paralysed) 'giant', and later lays a good many eggs on it. Her larvae in the chrysalis stage are parasites on it; their mother licks them and stays with them. Then the maggots spin their silken cocoons, and after leaving these, sometimes directly on leaving them, the brothers (which often emerge first) copulate with their sisters. Sometimes the mother too copulates with her sons. The sisters may lay their eggs also on the original prey, so the mother insect 'lives to see grandchildren', an important element in 'social life'. There are no lasting bonds, however, for the children disperse

51

when mature. Another peculiarity of *Scleroderma* is that both male and female insects can appear in two variants, with or without wings; and this is the beginning of that 'polymorphism' which, further developed, leads to the caste system of working and soldier insects.

These are examples of isolated elements which in combination with others would make social groups possible. But there are indeed many elements to be combined before a fully social form of animal life can be developed, and the problem of its evolution is very complex. One of the most recent summaries of our knowledge on the subject states laconically: 'In fact we know of no certain transitions between solitary and social life (among insects).'

Some of the phenomena of swarming are also of this sub-social kind, as with insects like dragonflies and butterflies whose social life is otherwise limited to reproduction processes. The causes of swarming are mysterious, and research is handicapped by the very nature of the phenomena: you cannot simply look for them and study them at will, or even let them happen. But of course such mass migrations, which are similar to swarming, occur regularly in forms of animal life at a higher level of development, as with birds, fishes, seals and whales. Such migrations are therefore an extreme variant of normal group-forming, and although full of unresolved problems, are no more mysterious than other instances where members of the same species gather in pairs or groups—in fact, than social life generally.

Among other examples of swarming, locust swarms are mysterious to the biologist because locusts otherwise show no true phenomena of social life. They have, however, been investigated with some thoroughness.

Swarming in its drastic form occurs with few species of locust. With these species it occurs in the course of great reproduction cycles of about four to six years on average, during which several generations are produced. Such a cycle starts with a generation which in its way of life is hardly distinguishable from other locusts (solitary form). The next generation may live more gregariously, 'forma transiens congregans', as biologists call it. The next batch of locusts may then be the destructive swarmers. When they have finished their great migrations, they disperse, thinned out of course by lack of food and by attacks on them, but also under the compulsion of changes in their metabolism. Their immediate offspring again show a tendency towards solitary life ('forma transiens dissocians'), and they are then followed by the more harmless solitary forms.

With some species the internal causes which cause such changes are apparent from the change of structure: e.g. *Locusta migratoria* (to be found even in Southern Europe) in its solitary but not its swarm variants is characterised by distinguishing marks between the sexes. The colouring of solitary and swarm variants may be very different from each other, the young (or 'nymphs') of the latter showing more lively colours and patterns (*Schistocerca gregaria*), which then disappear with the moults that lead to sexual maturity. The way the eggs develop is also different; with some species the eggs of the swarm variant have to go through an obligatory rest period. But the behaviour differences are particularly vital for our problem: the solitary forms (apart from the act of reproduction) will cut themselves off from other members of their species, like most of their relatives, whereas the individuals of the gregarious forms seek each other out, not only as fully winged mature insects, but in the nymph state before they can fly. Besides this tendency to union there is an unusual tendency to imitate other members of the species: when one insect makes a movement or changes direction, many of its neighbours will at once follow suit. This imitation occurs under the influence of optical stimuli, which lead to reflex actions through their connection with nerves. Such 'optomotor' reactions eventually reach an amazing regularity of behaviour in large swarms and are thus an essential factor in causing the swarms and carrying through the great migrations.

An examination of the processes of metabolism show that

these occur with higher intensity in the swarm generations. The terrific increase in greed is one part of this change, another being the increased production of yellow and black pigments; though these should be thought of partly as excretions which the insect has been storing within its skin.

Mutual attraction and compulsive imitation—two important factors in social life—are to be seen with these locusts in a particular phase of the life cycle; and there is a curious circular process which we shall be meeting again and again in observing social phenomena. Changed behaviour is the consequence of a changed metabolism, in our example attraction instead of dissociation: because the insects have a highly developed nervous system, they are capable of immediate imitation. Their activities and metabolism are mutually effective: the continual presence of stimuli presented by group life also makes for more group life.

Since these simple social relations occur even with the unwinged locust nymphs, they too will set out on devastating migrations, and once they start, there is no stopping them. Locusts periodically swarm, therefore, not because an isolated insect, which in itself would live a solitary life, has a 'change of mind', but because generations of insects have been fashioned with special peculiarities of behaviour: a tendency to isolation is replaced by a tendency to congregation.

*　　　*　　　*

The attraction of individuals to each other is the basic phenomenon of social life; and even for dragonflies, as we have seen, this social factor is primary for life itself. The individual in isolation is always secondary, the structure typical of the species goes beyond the individual. But before the social factor can be manifested, there must always be an instrument which allows single members of the same species to find each other. Such instruments are familiar to us from our knowledge of the higher animals, as from our own experience; but the familiar often proves the least truly 'known', and is sometimes too readily taken for granted.

As a matter of fact, although we cannot go into it here, the simplest forms of encounter confront us with the problem of what *causes* attraction, the first of all social stimuli, the 'lowest common multiple' even of higher social life. Certainly our human meetings are bound up with the method by which people find and later recognise each other.

It is only on the basis of attraction that divisions, rivalries and struggles for power, dominations and subjections, are possible. I have for years had an impressive demonstration of the fact in the place where I am writing this chapter. Before me the blue expanse of Villefranche Bay near Nice is spread out in the glittering sunlight. In this bay I have time and again gone catching the most beautiful and strange creatures of the high seas, such as jelly-fish and sea-snails, which quite exceptionally appear here very near the shore: a transparent world which is enthralling to anybody who once becomes involved with it—but its magic is another story.

In my early years of studying nature I had to find favourable places for catching these creatures of the sea's surface. As the great herring-gulls fed on them as well as on fishes, we used to head for parts of the bay where there were most gulls swimming or circling—hoping that we should there find a particularly good catch: for a gull's sharp eye was surely the best 'intelligence' for fishing biologists. But the result of our youthful strategy was always lamentable. The surface of the sea where the gulls swam was as empty as anywhere else, and if we found the jelly-fish and sea-snails at all, it would be in some quite unexpected place. I thus gradually learnt an impressive elementary lesson about the basic behaviour rules of the beautiful white birds which had so much disappointed us: herring-gulls are always in places where other herring-gulls are found—this is the only reason there need be for them to congregate. Such an observation is very simple, I know, but it may be a good thing to register once more that rule of social life which for all its simplicity is really full of problems: the fact that social life rests on a primary attraction between the individuals of a species. The instruments which ensure this attraction are tremendously varied. From the simplest but 'specific' unmistakable stimulus, perhaps conveyed by chemical substances, to the complicated but equally unmistakable 'specific' stimulating figure, the 'image' of another member of the species, they travel the whole scale and range of sensory life, and their study splits up into all the questions of general biology.

True social life is only possible among the more highly organised animals. Its place in the general life of a species, its relationship to the life of the individual animal and to the tasks of preserving the species, are so many-sided that we must try to clarify these differences systematically. The more our knowledge advances, it is true, the more difficult this seems. But as the survey of the system is continually changing and yet makes it easier for each generation of research workers to master the connections between different forms, so after many vain attempts a rational order of social phenomena among animals will in time be developed.

Tinbergen in 1953 produced in his survey an important characteristic, making possible the first general division of social forms: into those which occur through differentiation and those which occur through integration. The former is realised in extreme form in the 'insect colonies': the members of the society stem from one mother, and the distribution of work, the social interplay of the members in the colony, is essentially innate differentiation of blood relatives. The latter occurs through the coming together of members of a species which are not blood relatives but which form a society through integration of ways of behaviour. *Staying* together may be considered the genetic characteristic of the former type, *coming* together that of the second. This division is not hard and fast, of course, and there are cases where each type overlaps into the other; but it gives a first general direction.

*   *   *

The great 'insect colonies', which come into being through

differentiation, have been described in special works so often and so thoroughly that we may take many details of them as familiar. I am referring to them here only by way of comparison, to help put the societies of vertebrates in the right perspective of social life.

Whether the insect 'people' is founded by a 'queen', who is mated once in her life (as with bees), or by a 'royal couple', who stay together (as with termites), the amazing associations formed by these insects are always societies of blood relatives. They may incorporate different species as 'slaves', but such periodical integration is a separate and marginal problem, which we will leave on one side. Their basic existence depends on the fact that they stem from one mother and that they are assigned to the functions of bringing up young. A division of labour, which expresses itself also in the separation of castes, is realised through innate responses at appropriate stages of development and under various outside influences.

Innate reactions: the egg which develops can be destined by heredity to be male or female. With bees the males are fated to become drones; the fate of the females is decided by the feeding which the working insects give them: special food causes the ovaries to develop and fertile female insects are formed, whereas with poorer feeding they remain under-developed and become working bees. We should not imagine that this decision through feeding means 'higher development' for the nurture of queens and 'lower' for working insects. That is an over-simplification, since the 'more' and 'less' applies only to the sexual organs and the corresponding behaviour patterns. Moreover, these poor 'neuters' have a much more highly developed brain and sensory organisation than have the sexual forms, and they achieve here the greatest development. The process of caste-forming is really 'differentiation' in several directions, not merely stopping at various stages of a line of development.

The order of this 'family state', once formed, sees to it that the inherited dispositions are always fully exploited for various functions, so that there are always sexual, worker and soldier bees. There is thus an association of relatives with different functions, which the species needed for its continued existence. This sort of social organisation may last a very long time—in the termite colonies from 12 to 15 years, with *Nasutitermes* even a century (Grassé, 1949); with *Bellicositermes* too the age of a queen is put at about 80 years. The forming of such societies may be accompanied by swarming—in very different variants.

Swarming in the bee colonies is a genuine social phenomenon: the hive divides into two colonies, one staying in the old home but adopting a new queen, the other—the 'swarm'—flying off with the old queen in search of a new home.

With termites the winged insects of both sexes leave the termitary *en masse*; they are thus united at the start. But their social urge is replaced by reproduction factors. 'While swarming the insects separate, and the swarm gradually scatters like smoke climbing into the air. At first they all fly roughly in the same direction, but they soon disperse and land in very different places. The swarming of the termites is doubtless a collective phenomenon —but each "swarmer" behaves as an individual, flies on his own account, and knows nothing of his companions' (Grassé, 1942). Quite different is a special way of founding new colonies described by Grassé and Noirot (1948), which is a true social phenomenon like the swarming of bees, and is called 'sociotomy': 'A considerable part of the population leaves the termitary: a long column, in which all castes are to be found, including the "royal couple" and winged social insects ready to swarm. The column may split up further, and thus comes to found new colonies, whether with the old royal couple or with new royal couples developing from among worker insects.'

Societies which come into being through differentiation include individual social forms among vertebrates: true families conditioned by care for their young, as may be found among fishes, birds and mammals. There are parent-families, when the young have ties with both parents; mother-families, where the father is excluded from the bringing up of young; and father-families, where the father alone looks after the young, and the mother, once she has laid her eggs, has no more part in family life. All three variants are equally 'natural', and we have no reason to rate one of them (e.g. the mother-family) higher than the others or consider it the original one. Each has its value as a possible system of highly organised care for the young; and in this sphere there are as many converging points as in the adaptation of forms of life to their physical environment. In water, for instance, reptiles once by some unknown means reached the fish structure of the Ichthyosaurus; while land mammals once similar to the predators reached the extreme fish structure of the dolphin furthest removed from any mammal form: similarly different groups of creatures have developed converging ways of looking after their young. In a stimulating study in 1948 Peters described this family structure as 'convergence' of behaviour; we may follow up some of his findings.

The way in which completely different groups, like birds and fishes, may develop similar condition of caring for young is shown by the striking parallels in the behaviour of sticklebacks and certain Australian megapodes, which have both developed the same type of father-family. The male stickleback builds a nest in a strongly-defended nesting area. When a mature female passes, he entices her with characteristic movements to the nest's entrance, encourages her to swim into the nest and lay eggs, then fertilises the eggs in the nest. Afterwards he drives her out, and she has nothing more to do with the young. The father looks after them, supplying them with water rich in oxygen by fanning, and guarding them with great care till they leave the nest.

With the Australian megapode *Leipoa ocellata* the cock builds a nesting-ground from vegetables, which he covers with a huge heap of sand. He watches over this mound, and the female may only lay her eggs within this nest (incidentally, they are placed on end). Here too the male drives out the female, and during the nine weeks in which the embryos grow without actual hatching, he sees to the regulation of the temperature: in the early morning he scrapes away the topmost layer of sand, lets the remainder be warmed for hours by the sun, and in the afternoon piles the warm sand back again into a nest-mound.

A quite different 'pattern of behaviour' is illustrated by the parallel of a mother-family in fishes and birds. With the perch *Nannacara anomala*, the mother attends to the laying of the eggs,

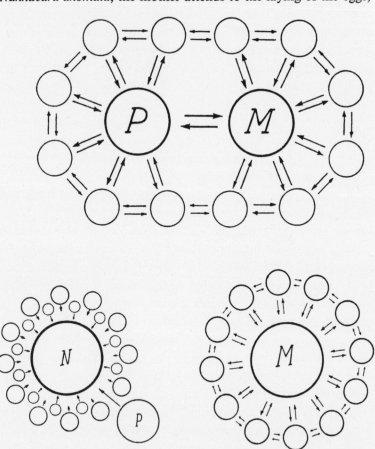

FIG. 9. Schematic representation of family structures among fishes. P = father; M = mother; N = nest. The unmarked circles: young fish. Various sizes of circles show different ages of young looked after at the same time. Arrows show most important relational directions. Above: parents-family. Below, left: father-family (nest as centre). Below, right: mother-family (mother as centre) (after Peters, 1948).

fans them with fresh water and looks after the young fish when out of the egg, which swim around under her guidance and protection, thereby leaving the spawning-ground but still keeping the closest contact with their mother.

Whereas in the examples of father-families mentioned above the nest is the vital centre for the young, in the mother-family it is the mother herself. This behaviour in *Nannacara* corresponds exactly, of course, to that of the hen who hatches her eggs and leads her chicks without help from the cock.

Peters showed in 1950 that such forms of family are established through further typical aspects of co-operation. In the parent-family, for instance, one variant can be clearly distinguished in which the mother alone attends to the actual care of the young, while the father watches over the nest and surroundings and brings food for the whole family. In true mother-families (as we find with ducks) the male may maintain his ties with the mother, but have no contact with the young. Conversely the father may look after the young, as with labyrinthine fishes like the paradise fish, where the female settles at the edge of the territory guarded by the father.

The system of relationship of forms, so carefully investigated and confirmed by zoologists, is thus criss-crossed by different systems of similarities, convergences of structure and behaviour, which other biologists are investigating with equal zeal. It is only when different systems are woven in together that we shall be able to appreciate the intricate pattern of nature as a whole.

*　　*　　*

The evidence of 'social structures' appearing as clearly recognisable types in quite different groups leads us to another kind of structural correspondence. This time it is the way in which a particular function is carried out with very different means and yet shows an amazing similarity of result.

Let us return for a moment to the father-family (like the stickleback), in which the father builds the nest and is left with the whole responsibility for the eggs which have been laid. We will now compare this process with that of the hippocamps (or sea-horses) and their nearest neighbours, the syngnaths (or pipefish), a group of fishes which is incidentally very near the stickleback in fish classification.

The father here, with his dying act, takes over the eggs into a breeding organ at the side of his belly, in which the whole spawn grows. They do not leave it until they have emerged from the egg and become fishes. The worm-pipefish (*Nerophis*) show us the simplest way within this group: while the male and female are mating, the eggs stick to the male's belly, where they are held by an adhesive skin excretion in a narrow furrow; they are freely exposed to the water. With pipefish the two parallel folds in the belly are very pronounced; their outer edges stick together after taking the eggs, and the father's skin provides all the oxygen needed. The sea-horses, however, form a regular belly pocket, which is only open in front and can be closed by a sphincter muscle. The fathers do more than those of the other groups: they provide blood for the eggs lying in the pocket in hollows of the skin, and seem to excrete various substances for the benefit of the spawn.

All this is far from what we think of as social life, yet it is still somehow a type of father-family; only the business of nest-building and looking after the young is here replaced and carried out by organs of the male body. There is one more way in which it is like the stickleback: with both species the urge to take over the eggs is innate in the male fish. It would be easy enough to miss the point that in one case the father's care for the young is 'managed' by extremely complicated actions, in the other by equally complicated processes of skin-change.

Here is another example of different solutions to the same problem. First, many spiders build their webs with complicated arrangements for opening and shutting, like regular doors. Secondly, a genus of bees, *Halictus*, lives in sand-webs, where the door is provided by a live insect with its body. As Fabre reported: 'When *Halictus* comes back from visiting her young and wants to fly into her hollow, you can see a sort of flap, which was keeping the gate closed, go quickly down and leave the entrance free. As soon as she is in, it shuts again; the same thing happens when she is flying out . . . it is a *Halictus* bee which has been made doorkeeper or *concierge*. This is the founder of the family, the mother of the females now flying out, the grandmother of the larvae inside the web. Unable to become mother a second time, she becomes a sort of guard to open up the dwelling and chase off intruders.'

Thirdly, there are species of tropical ants (*Colobopsis*) in which a special structural variant forms with a flat-shaped growth, the colour of bark, on its head. This is like a trap-door which fits exactly into the apertures through which the colony's passages bored into plants open outwards. 'If a worker wishes to leave the nest to seek food, she gives the soldier a sign with her feelers, whereupon he steps aside and lets her pass, immediately afterwards resuming his post as living door. Returning to the nest, members of the species must again "ask for permission to enter" in feeler-language.' (Buytendijk). Here again the same function of 'doormanship' is fulfilled in one case by a form of behaviour, in another by the special destiny of the colony's mother insect at a particular phase of her life, and in a third by a structural change and specialisation in part of a society.

There is another essential point which emerges from these strange parallels of achievement by such very different means. Neo-Darwinists may explain the individual cases as the outcome of natural selection, random and purposeless; but the more closely we examine them together, the harder it becomes to see the original variation in this light. That seems to go back into a primordial darkness, which can yet be imagined as fraught with creative existence. If the geneticist or the development physio-logist says we are acquainted only with the chance variations we call mutations, I would readily agree. But if he goes on to say there are no other changes, he oversteps the competence of experimental biology and without the necessary qualifications sets himself up as a prophet.

*   *   *

The family life we have so far considered has led us to the sphere of vertebrates, but the social structures possible with them rest on the other principle of society-forming, the integration of members who need not be blood relatives. At the base of all integration lies the elementary phenomenon of attraction between members of the species, as we saw in its simplest form with the swarming of locusts, the nesting colonies and 'dormitories' of sand-wasps. These simple forms of social life present biologists with many separate problems, into which we are only gradually penetrating, but it looks as if by solving them we may add considerably to our understanding of social phenomena.

One of these problems concerns the deeper reasons for a phenomenon noted by Hediger (since 1941): that simple social life among animals may occur in two different ways, through the individuals either keeping a fixed distance from each other or pressing close together. As an example of the former we may think of swallows congregated on telegraph wires in autumn or gulls spread out on the rails of a ship; for the latter we have parrots—like the 'love-birds' where one is said to pine away at the death of its mate—and also weaver-birds. Among mammals, boars, many rodents, many apes and lemurs are extreme 'contact-creatures', while many ruminants are 'distance creatures' (Plates 8 and 9).

Below the Murchison Falls of the Nile in Central Africa a 'distance order' of crocodiles (which live there in incredible masses) was described thus by Pitman (in 1931): 'If you look down into the water on a calm day, you will be amazed at the regular placing shown by row on row of crocodiles: like warships they lie at intervals of about fifty feet and with three hundred feet distance between the rows, which stretch from one bank to the other.' We are familiar with the same thing among many species of fish. Trout, for instance, have been observed in up to eight rows in completely military formation, all with their heads facing upstream, all keeping their place and distance through subtle swimming movements. With many deep-sea fishes, such as mackerel, the distances in the shoal are more or less constant, though a shoal may sometimes move closer together as a panic reaction; but they will soon resume normal distances again (Plate 10).

Social research begins by establishing phenomena and their extensiveness, and in describing them seeks only to say what has been observed. Nothing has yet been observed to tell us what makes one group a 'distance' creature and another a 'contact' creature; probably this may be decided for different groups, perhaps even for those more closely related, by completely different factors in their sensory life.

The working out of the conditions mentioned above is shown by most breeding colonies of birds. After great migrations the birds of a species congregate in a chosen place, often the haunt of the species from time immemorial (we will ignore for the moment the possible mixing of species). In some cases they come either solitary or in groups without necessarily forming pairs. Among the thousands which congregate in this way there will certainly be birds born from the same parents, but they do not know each other as blood relatives—this is not what brings them together; and even when pairs form, they are usually birds from different origins. Immense numbers of birds will thus often be living in a very narrow area, on cliff or rock or dune, perhaps divided up by sex—though such a division is very often indistinguishable before they have reached complete maturity. This goes not only for the human observers, but for the birds themselves, which sometimes 'declare' their sex to each other by an elaborate ceremonial on reaching maturity.

Attraction of members of the same species brings these colonies together; innate behaviour patterns peculiar to each species allow the building of many-sided relations between the mates in a pair, between parents and young, but also between families and in extreme cases even between single individuals. This structure is possible without blood relationship, whereas in the 'differentiation societies' every embryo grows towards that structure of which it will later become a functioning part. Thus with our breeding colony the structure of relations must be put together again and again through the behaviour of individual birds which have never met before. One of the peculiarities of such integrated societies is that they may periodically break up in favour of other groupings or even of completely solitary existence. The forming of these societies is not governed solely by the needs of reproduction; the attraction between single members of a species and the need for an individual territory are both bound up in a great many ways with the urge to form pairs and to rear young (Plates 11 to 13).

*   *   *

Thanks to the brilliant field studies of F. Fraser Darling in the Scottish Highlands, we have detailed information on the way red deer form groups, which illustrates the variety of social forms possible within a single species. Deer-herds indeed are among the best investigated of mammal societies.

First there are the herds of hinds, social units of strong cohesion which rest on the bond of the young with their mother, continuing till their third year. Each herd is led by one of the older hinds, whose leadership may last undisputed as long as she lives. She almost always has a fawn with her, and she reproduces regularly; this is probably bound up with her leadership, which she would lose without this sign of 'normality'. She is continuously anxious and watchful, the most alert member of the herd, however much the other hinds help in 'security precautions'. In favourable areas of Scotland such a herd sometimes numbers up to 200 animals altogether, which inhabit a large territory in groups of 30 to 40 and are seldom to be seen completely united.

When fawns are born, the mother drives off the older fawns for the time being: the yearlings take this as a new sort of game, and the two-year-olds accept the situation. About this time the young stags leave the herd of hinds.

The herd of stags is a much looser association of egocentric males without any clear leadership. These herds also roam much more, and sometimes split up into age-groups when resting or grazing. The rutting animals sometimes go off to form their separate reproduction groups during the rutting season.

In the reproduction period each stag founds a kind of harem: he will sometimes keep a group of hinds together, although never actually leading them—like a sheep-dog with a flock of sheep. The hinds are still led, guarded and watched over by their female leader. The stag warns her if there is danger, and the other hinds go into cover with her. He may follow or go his own way. The harem group is thus a strange duality: in many respects a small herd of hinds, in others a unit temporarily dominated by the stag.

The state of the harem can change very quickly, as one example from Darling's observations will show: on 28th September, 1934, there was a particularly handsome stag with 77 hinds and fawns. He was very active, and kept circling the group and driving off his rivals, who yet remained very close to the herd. Two days later, in the same area, there were only 46 under his 'command'; three other rutting stags had formed harems nearby, each with about 10 to 12 hinds, though their domains were much smaller than his. On 4th October their harems had grown considerably, and the original lord and master was followed by only 23 animals; by 7th October the number had sunk to 11, his activities having also conspicuously decreased. 10 other stags had meanwhile founded and increased their harems.

The example of the stags has lately been supplemented by a parallel detailed study of the American elk (*Cervus canadensis nelsoni*). (Marg. Altmann, 1952).

The reproduction societies formed by sea-lions and seals are extremely strange. When not rutting, they herd together in the sea in larger or smaller groups. We have recently gained closer knowledge of this deep-sea period in the life of the famous northern fur-seals (bear-seals, *Arctocephalus ursinus*) inhabiting the Pribilof Islands in the Bering Sea. It has been carefully investigated by K. W. Kenyon and F. Wilke in 1943, and the precision of their results is again mostly due to the markings which allowed them to pick out the individual from the mass. We now know that these seals leave the islands at very different times, sometimes as early as October, sometimes not till December. In a few cases they stay near their home waters—especially the bulls—but others travel over 3,000 miles on the high seas, though seldom more than 55 miles from the coast. So on their winter migrations these bear seals travel from the Aleutians to the Japanese Islands and on the other side of the Pacific to the shores of Mexico.

They are isolated by their travels; we meet them either singly or in bands of 5 to 15 seals, hardly ever more than that. The mortality rate in the first years is very high: from the yearling calves 70 per cent. succumb in the first three years to the various hazards of seal life.

During their sea-trip, seals of different origins come together, and they are only separated by the approach of the mating season; they then keep strictly to their native coasts, where they mostly look for their exact birthplace. As soon as they reach land, their social structure (in the case of many species) becomes strikingly rigid. But the forms of their social life are unusually varied from species to species.

The sea-lions of the Falkland Islands (*Otaria byronia*) land at different parts of the coast in two distinct groups, those which have and those which have not reached sexual maturity—the latter including many bulls which have not yet succeeded in winning a cow. Both bulls and cows live in the herds of those capable of reproduction; most of the cows have mated the year before and are now pregnant, but the others are still unmated. By aggressive behaviour the bulls mark out a strip of coast as their territory, where they are sole rulers, and collect round them a severely guarded harem of cows, on average about nine to one bull. The rules are very strict: no cow may go back into the sea before being served. Then the pregnant mothers are served, as soon as the calf conceived the year before has been born. When all the cows have been served, the bull's aggressiveness diminishes rapidly, and the little group gradually breaks up.

The Antarctic sea-elephants have harems of about 12 to 20 cows, and here too the bull defends a territory, which may start fierce battles between rivals (Plates 15 and 16).

In extreme contrast to these polygamous societies, there are other seal societies in whose herds there is complete promiscuity without any sign of harem forming or defence of a territory. The Atlantic seal (*Halichoerus grypus*) shows a strange mean between the two. The first arrivals among the bulls do form a small harem, but during the weeks of rutting several bulls may go off after a group of cows. In one case it was observed that for six weeks a bull kept together a group of 17 cows, defending his territory against intruders, while another group of 24 cows were followed in two and a half months by 4 bulls. It is hard to decide in which direction the Atlantic seals have moved, from promiscuity to the forming of harems, or the other way round—the gradual breaking up of a polygamous group.

The polygamous group led by a male is sometimes relatively stable, as with some antelopes, though here too it may be formed only during the rutting season. But a lasting polygamous society is established, for instance, by groups of water-buck (*Kobus defassa*) in Parc Albert in the Belgian Congo, as was observed between 1931 and 1940 (Hediger, 1951).

One last example will show the different forms of social life which may occur over the years in a single genus. Bats, which are strikingly gregarious, sometimes collect in masses at rest periods at their favourite haunts. When assembled, they make for their day-dormitories and hang head downwards in roof frames, caves or (in the tropics) on trees. Besides this they often hibernate in caves—both sexes together—in immense numbers.

Reproduction, however, brings a special note to their rich social life: the females' confinement. Bats mate in autumn, and after mating the females stay with the males in their selected winter quarters. The egg cells only mature in the spring when they come out of hibernation, the spermatozoa are at last mobilised and only now achieve their destiny of fertilisation. At this time the female bats are seized by an urge to get away from 'male society' and fly off together to communal quarters. Often these are a good distance away; some mouse-eared bats (*Myotis myotis*), for instance, which had been marked for identification, migrated 30 or 40 miles from where they had been hibernating. Churches and the attics of old houses are favourite 'confinement places', because of their even temperature: without using up too much energy, the mothers can find the warmth needed for their young to develop. So here the female bats spend the bright day, squeezed tightly together; there may be isolated males among them, but only very occasionally.

*   *   *

We may well conclude this first survey of animal societies by comparing them with our own societies, to bring out the many features there are in common between them and also the striking contrasts.

The structure of human life in general is social, as with all higher animals. Man comes to 'sociability' not by 'arrangement', by rational decision, but from the natural, primary disposition which he shares with all higher animals. Attraction to other members of the species precedes all hostility and repulsion; solitariness is always secondary, a flight from the natural bond, and our imaginations are gripped by Robinson Crusoe tales just because the solitary state is so out of the ordinary. Moreover, not only do Crusoes need a shipwreck to make their tales credible, but their experience of civilisation and a social order is implicit in everything they do.

But what *is* our natural state of society? There is no such thing. In all stages of man's social life there is a world alien from, and opposed to, nature. What is natural to him is civilisation, and the form of our society is one of its most important achievements—'natural artificiality', as Plessner calls it. Reports are still sometimes made on the lives of remote people as if they were completely 'children of nature' and comparable with wild animals. This is nonsense, of course, for all human groups existing today have complicated social structures, as ethnologists have conclusively shown. With this illusion destroyed, our latter-day neo-Darwinists try to find our 'natural state' among the higher primates, the mammals most closely related to man, all of which exhibit many forms of social life.

But then the highest apes have different types of society. One male chimpanzee rules over 12 to 15 females and their progeny, one male gorilla over about 4 females on average and 8 to 10 immature young gorillas; the East Asian orang-outang also lives in such a large polygamous society.

Gibbons, on the other hand (thoroughly studied by Carpenter in Siam), are organised in monogamous families of father, mother and up to four offspring from babies to adolescents of about six to eight years at oldest. The family has a territory which remains very stable, and is defended against other gibbon families: through living together and long familiarity with each other, they form a very firmly established unit.

If the biologist looks among other groups of apes, he finds long-tailed monkeys and baboons in larger units containing several harems, each led by a male, also units of elderly males excluded from harem-forming and of males which are not yet fully mature. The South American spider-monkeys (*Ateles geoffreyi*) live in large polygamous families, generally consisting of two adult males, four mature females and up to six children, of which two are still following the mother; but here too there are also separate hordes of males.

The howling monkeys (*Alouatta palliata*) live in an actual clan system, with the males leading by turns and the females belonging to all males: there are on average three adult males, eight females, four immature apes and three offspring still dependent on their mother. The whole 'clan' defend their territory fiercely, their howling being an essential means of demonstrating ownership.

From the monogamous family, then, to extreme polygamous organisation, such is the picture of the higher primates presented to the biologist who would seek among them the original form of human society. The choice he makes will depend on the assumptions he brings to the search. If he is a resolute defender of the naturalness of our monogamous society, it may be enough for him that this is 'already' present among the primates. If he sympathises with the possibility of polygamy, he may tend to stress a natural tendency of males or of both sexes in that direction. He may also be so convinced of particular theories of man's origin that he makes the anthropoids an exclusive criterion: in that case the apes nearest to ourselves demonstrate the social structure (once typical for man) of a polygamous family led by one male. If on the other hand he believes that the revolutionary break-away of the earliest hominids from the anthropoids must have taken place very early, as far back as the tertiary age, then he will think it quite possible that lower apes also show significant features of those hominids, while gorillas, orang-outang and chimpanzee perhaps represent a separate development in their forms of society.

In the last twenty years biologists have realised increasingly that research into human origins will remain an unlimited field, in which isolated facts shine out more or less brightly against a dark background, like stars in the night sky. I cannot stress sufficiently how hard it is to give any answer to the interwoven questions which the problem of origins involves.

This is why the behaviour research-worker today cannot offer such bold and dogmatic solutions as were given in the prime of Darwinism; he is far more concerned to grasp the relativity of societies among all higher animals. We are not looking for an original 'society' but for how and where the first elements of social life appear. Only an intimate knowledge of these elements, from which we are still far removed, will one day enable us to ask which of these fundamental social structures was probably the pre-hominid state. At present we can say nothing conclusive about it, and can only bring out individual features the significance of which we are fairly capable of assessing. We can at least be sure that social environment has a vital importance for primates in general, and that living continuously with other members of the species and being familiar with a group play a large part in individuals' preservation and development. Bourlière expressly emphasises (1952) the tendency to increasing independence of physical environment and correspondingly greater dependence on social environment.

Although the bond between mother and child is most natural, of course, in the social structure of larger groups, the way it fits into our human society is by no means natural, but is a matter of convention and adaptation, in fact a part of the 'natural artificiality'.

There is another important attribute of our social structure which we share with the higher mammals: all our natural abilities are appropriate to life in a small group, where clearly defined relations can exist between its members. This is the social environment in which we function best, assessing our own relative abilities, allowing them play and bringing them into tolerable balance with the qualities and defects of others. This does not apply only to living together at peace, but also to situations of tension, self-assertion and submission, as can be seen in higher animal groups.

Thanks to civilisation we are today very far removed from such a state, and this has brought us into almost insoluble difficulties. Thousands of years ago the urges and emotions we still live by, if not always helpful, would yet in a small group have been mostly harmless and non-destructive; whereas today, with human relations forming a world-wide nexus and an agglomeration too big to be grasped as a group, such urges and emotions have become dangerous, threatening the preservation of the species. We have to find out how to adapt innate social forms, and find new structures of relationship, which will maintain the value of small groups and fully realise the natural tendencies towards them, while bringing them into new harmony with the inevitable increase in world population.

One feature which all primate groups have in common is the smallness of their litter: lemurs, gibbons and all the anthropoids have only one offspring. Its state is very advanced at birth, with active sensory organs, open eyes, and a nervous system so elaborate that it can be compared with foals, kids and lambs which walk immediately after birth. Compared, of course, to the original primates living on trees, these forms do not leave their mother, and her body is where they first clamber around. In any case we must attend very closely to this peculiarity of development in primates, because between it and human development there are striking differences and striking similarities.

A characteristic of the primates which is very important for reproduction and social life is the absence of a rutting season. Many species of lemurs reproduce all the year round, and this seems to be the general rule with higher primates, though some species at large may reach a peak of reproduction at a particular time of year. At any rate the anthropologist who tries to fix the origins of social life among men, and possible pre-hominid conditions, must reckon with the fact that the suspension of sexual periods is a general pre-human feature of life among primates. Important though it is, we know very little of the effect it has on their social life.

It is an essential feature of humanity that we have fitted the elements we share with the higher animals into a structure of society. We have at birth a diffuse, inherited capacity for speech, but must learn a particular language through social intercourse; in the same way we have a general, largely unformalised capacity for social contact, but our norms of society are decided by the society we are born, learn and grow up in. These norms, which were not of our choosing, may have the force of natural law for some, while others, who reject them, are led to seek

changes in the society. This is the special thing about civilisation, our 'artificial' second nature.

Whereas animals' social forms are only changed by hereditary mutations, man's social forms are continually being changed
by historic decisions or crises. The elements we sometimes call
stable, like forms of government and religious fundamentals and
reverence for ancestors, are always part of a tradition peculiar
to man, the conscious and deliberate effort, instilled by education,
to maintain existing conventions. Its converse, radical revolu-
tion, is just as much the work of conscious will, secret planning,
purposeful upbringing and the attempt to create a new tradition.

By our very nature we are called ever and again to create and
preserve new social forms. The drive to find these corresponds
to the animal's drive towards hereditary forms; but the finding
of them is our freedom—and our constant duty. So the search
for natural forms of human society should not be directed backwards, in vain longing for a vanished state of nature, but forwards
towards new forms, fortified by the knowledge that any special
kind of 'nature' created by us can be a true goal. The grace of
the dance, for instance, is not simply natural, but achieves an
extra gracefulness through the control and organisation of natural
movements.

That the drive to find forms of society in freedom is part of
our nature, is suggested by the fact that the conditions we are
born in seem directed towards this objective. In comparison
with every group of mammals we have a very prolonged youth, a
period which they must devote to attaining sexual maturity, but
in which we have far more lessons to learn besides that: we have
our innate and life-long capacity for creative activity, for transforming our way of life and for intellectual expansion. Compared with the higher mammals we have twice as long a life span,
so that several generations can live together and be integrated
with each other.

The most striking among these marks of our civilised state is
the peculiarity of our early development. Instead of continuing

in the protection of a mother's body as long as would accord with
our superior brain development, we are born as helpless creatures
—in contrast to the state in which most mammals are born.
Instead of beginning our life with well-developed limbs and the
ability to move as freely as grown-ups of the species—like deer-
calves, foals, elephant cubs, young giraffes, whales, dolphins and
seals—we have a special extra-uterine first year very different
from our further development, during which we gradually learn
both to stand and to talk through social contact; we also learn
purposeful action, the specific human fashion of controlling
environment. None of these three faculties will be fully achieved
if social contact is lacking or inferior. That is one of the reasons
why biologists are eager to bring out both the correspondences
and the differences between the behaviour of men and of the
animals most closely related to him.

4

Organs of Communication

LYING IN THE grass on a summer day, we are lulled by the chirping of grasshoppers. If we overcome the lethargy induced by their monotonous chant, we can see the strange way in which relationship is established here between individuals of a species. On close examination we find that these grasshoppers have different instruments for making their chirping noise. Some do it with their wings, others by rubbing their wing-covers on the back of their legs. Both sexes have hearing organs, but the females are almost always dumb, so that it is only the males which chirp. Their chirping is intended both to attract females and to keep rivals in check. Male grasshoppers will chirp alternately, but if they come too close the chirping will change to a note of rivalry, whereupon both will move farther away again. At this distance the 'chirping response' takes place, with both insects stimulating each other to song. The hearing organs which make such contact possible are situated either in the front legs (with long-horned grasshoppers) or in the base of the abdomen (with short-horned grasshoppers).

The encounter we have witnessed here works towards preserving the species, allowing male and female grasshoppers, which otherwise live in isolation, to find each other for reproduction purposes. The ending of isolation through sexual intercourse is, of course, one of the original and essential forms of social life. It is more than creatures of the same species meeting through a common external stimulus, such as moths which are drawn to a light or insects of another species gathering on a particular plant they feed on. The meeting which leads to reproduction presupposes a simple 'recognition' by members of the same species, based on the very structure of the species, especially a transmitter

77

(in this case the male grasshopper's chirping organ) and a receiver (both sexes' hearing organ).

Every fertilised egg-cell has a dual structure carrying the genes for receiving as well as transmitting apparatus. Which of the two is actually developed depends on whether male or female emerges. The structure of the species, represented by the bisexual egg-cell, creates an order which brings the two separated insects into a unity, and allows them to find each other by a means of communication in an environment where they cannot see each other at a distance. What is formed here in the service of reproduction, the sexual encounter, already carries within it the principle of all other kinds of meeting.

Although we should scarcely describe grasshoppers as 'social' insects, even in their isolation they are always part of a system of relationships, a system established in the structure of the species. When we talk of 'social life', we mean complex ways of relationship; but these too rest on the fact that all life organised in cells has a structure which transcends the individual.

With research into the organs which achieve relationship between living creatures, social biology enters the vast realm of the sensory organisation as 'receiving department' and as 'transmitting department'. A few examples will show how many patterns of relationship there are, and their very different degrees of intensity and social levels.

*   *   *

All forms of life which have a structure dependent on the combination of nucleus and protoplasm—that is, all animals and plants with one or many cells—are so made that they may find each other in the progenitive act. In the case of single sexual cells (when one-celled animals meet, that is, and also when egg and germ cells meet in higher organisms) the meeting may be ensured if the cells' transmitting structure forms special chemical substances and if their receiving structure is receptive to these substances within strict limits. We do not know if the substances work automatically, of if there is also a subjective 'perceiving' side.

Their effect has been studied in the last two decades with especial thoroughness in the reproduction processes of individual algae. The part played by such 'emission' of substances in the sexual encounter of higher organisms is attested by the observations of butterfly-collectors, who entice male moths from a considerable distance through material impregnated with the female's scent; this is an irresistible 'draw' for the male moths, who would otherwise be hard to find. In this case the 'receiving' is done by the feelers with their delicate barbs, much longer in the male than in the female, which are packed with organs of smell.

Scent-organs, which are often 'transmitters' in the service of the sexual encounter, may with higher organisms acquire a significance leading far beyond this connection into wider social relationships.

Emissions of scent as organs of encounter have a specially varied development among mammals—and the 'receivers' from the olfactory mucous membrane to the structures of the brain are correspondingly complicated. There is much evidence to show that the use of all kinds of glandular substances is one of the primitive means of communication. A marked characteristic in mammals even of simple and archaic general structure is the preponderance of their olfactory organs and of the region of the brain originally adapted to them. This stage of the organism is low, of course, in comparison with mammals in general, but very high in the general gradation of all animals. Smell has much fewer variations than have sight and hearing, and therefore much fewer possibilities of communication. It may be very varied among mammals, but in precise shades of difference it is far inferior to movements of the tail and body, and vocal or facial expressions —which therefore are often subtly combined with scent effects.

There are all the glands between ruminants' claws or in other parts of their feet, which give their spoor a special smell. Antelope and deer have pre-orbital glands (near the eyes), chamois have glands behind their brain, the secretions of which, through special innate ways of behaviour, they leave at certain places in their habitat as highly effective scents. Martens foul twigs with the secretions of their anal glands, and the American ground-squirrel sheds on branches and stones the secretions from the scent-glands on its back. The urine of the canine predators has a corresponding function for recognition, and the male hippopotamus sprinkles his surroundings intensively with urine and dung, distributing them with his tail. Many mammals, such as bears, bisons and others, impregnate their hides through rolling in urine and then rub favourite trees in their territory with this substance so that the trees without bark are strongly marked as their domain by smell as well as sight.

I have gone into some detail on this use of smell in the service of communication, because a veil has often been drawn, owing to the way human society has developed, over such 'low' and elementary functions as the passing of dung and urine. Despite the thorough knowledge of such functions gained by hunters, their great biological importance has only been recognised for about twenty-five years; thanks partly to the liberating effect of psycho-analysis, no doubt, research into this part of life is now regarded as normal and natural. (Uexküll and Sarris, 1931; Hediger, 1944, 1949.) H. Christoffel's work on the socio-psychological role of human urination brings an amazing wealth of evidence from human civilisation to confirm the results of purely biological research.

So much for scent as a means of communication, increasing the individual's effectiveness, providing the area he lives in with his individual mark, an extension of personal presence which is an essential part of all higher social relationships. Incidentally there is hardly an elementary function of the animal body, even if caused by the very lowest and most basic needs, which may not appear in the service of social relationships in higher ways of life. Vertebrates' breathing apparatus is transformed to produce voice; hair and feathers may bristle or be smoothed down not

Plate 9. Flock of migrating oyster-catchers *(Haematopus ostralegus)* on the beach. The wind makes the birds form ranks but not crowd together.

Photo: Eric Hosking.

Plate 10. *Haplochromis philander* (above), a mouth-brooding cichlid from South West Africa. The olive-grey female, which may be as much as 4 inches long, carries her brood in the much expanded oral cavity.

After Holly, Meincken and Rachow.

Trout (below) in closed ranks in a New Zealand stream.

Photo: H. B. MacDonald, from 'Zoologica', *New York.*

Plate 11. Brooding colony of sandwich tern *(Sterna sandvicensis)*.
Photo: Eric Hosking.

Plate 12. Brooding colony of gannet *(Sula bassana)*. The territories are small, but exactly spaced out: balance between opposing tendencies of gregariousness and segregation.   *Photo: Eric Hosking.*

only to conserve or reduce heat but also to communicate mood. Instead of merely being adapted for hearing, the ear muscle can express inner states such as fear, anger, aggressiveness, excitement. So we see the skin-glands and also the excretion of urine being used for communication; and the baby who in playful innocence enjoys and uses his faeces as strange plastic material reveals the same attitude, whereby hidden powers take control of such 'waste matter' to give it a new purpose and put it in the service of the highest forms of life.

Birds and mammals not only exploit the emission of chemical substances in the sexual sphere but have social organs developing therefrom with transmitting and receiving structure. This applies even to some fishes, such as minnows, which when wounded let off a substance into the water that is registered by other minnows through the organ of smell and causes a drastic inner change in the shoal. Besides at once taking flight, they remain thoroughly alarmed for hours or even days. The 'terror-substance', which is produced by the bite of a predator, thus becomes a literally 'alarming' substance with social significance.

Honey-bees too have a scent-gland on their hindquarters which has become a true social organ and emits a substance highly stimulating for other 'worker bees'. They can smell it from a long way off, so that it can help to draw newcomers to places where good stores of honey have already been found—though of course they are also drawn there by the scent of flowers carried by the other bees.

But in this highly developed form of society the system of relationships is enriched by optical means of communication, such as dances—which von Frisch and his colleagues have been investigating in detail for several decades, and which have been so often described that I need only refer to them briefly here. The 'round-dance' is a call to work very close to the hive. The possibilities for honey-gathering 50 to 100 yards away are given by another movement, the 'waggle dance', the pace of which is reduced according to the distance of the honey, though the actual movement remains just as sweeping. Dances in the hive have been observed when the honey supplies were 7 miles away, which shows the possible range of a bee colony. Still more amazing is the fact that the bees inside the hive can also tell the direction they must fly in, because they have a key to the dancing 'code'. Here is the key in von Frisch's words: 'A waggle dance upwards indicates that the food source lies in the direction of the sun. A waggle dance downwards indicates a feeding place in the opposite direction. A waggle dance to the right means that the food source is to be found to the right of the sun, and at such an angle to the right by which the waggle dance deviates from the vertical. A waggle dance to the left indicates a feeding place at a corresponding angle to the sun's position' (1942). The demonstrations which have led to these discoveries are among the most impressive achievements of modern biology, and should be read in von Frisch's own unique account (1941).

The bees can even get their directions by dancing when there is no sun visible, provided there is a patch of blue sky. For the latest advances in von Frisch's work have proved that bees (and other higher insects) find their bearings by the direction from which the polarised blue light of the sky oscillates and which is dependent on the sun's position. To describe how this is done goes beyond the framework of our discussion of social organs.

What concerns us now are these facts, proved by many experiments: first, the innate structure which forms in the individual insect's development is built on a co-ordinated system of emissions consisting in complicated stimuli, with movements and scents combining; second, the order of these various emissions is related by heredity to essential factors in the environment; and finally, the meaning of these exactly ordered emissions is already built into the nervous system of the species through the innate 'receiver' structure. The way in which relations with other members of the species are organised through innate faculties in each individual—independent of learning processes—is often called a 'bee language'; and certainly it goes far beyond the recognition of a sexual partner or other members of the species. It gives these other members information on individual experience of the environment with a precision which shows them how to find their way in that environment. Compared to the use of gestures and sounds, chemical and optical signals, simply to effect an encounter, the wealth of communication possible among bees would be great enough to merit the word 'language'—only it seems better to reserve that for human speech, our own unique means of communication.

The English biologist W. H. Thorpe, describing the waggle dance, remarks (1950): 'This performance of the worker hive bee is nothing more or less than elementary map-making and map reading, a symbolic activity in which the direction of action of gravity is symbolic of the direction of incidence of the sun's rays. We are forced to ask ourselves whether, apart from human faculties, there is anything comparable to this behaviour in the animal kingdom.'

Our knowledge of termites' means of communication is as fragmentary and hypothetical as it is extensive for bees, but even what has been learnt reveals important new aspects of social life. In contrast to the colonies of ants, bees and wasps, the fully developed termitary is inhabited by a great many so-called ergatoid (substitute) kings and queens as well as the original royal couple. While still larvae or nymphs these 'substitutes' can very quickly mature their embryonal sexual glands without changing their own immature form. Under stimuli we shall be referring to later, a larva's third stage is succeeded by the maturing of testes or ovaries and also of sexual apertures. Pigments form which make the eyes visible for the first time, and the hindquarters swell up enormously.

As soon as the royal couple (or one of them) dies, these substitute forms develop in the remotest corner of the termitary, in four or five weeks at the fastest. The first symptoms of their transformation can sometimes be seen a week after the king or queen's death (though it by no means always takes place with the eldest of the larvae capable of being transformed). This process has been called social regulation, and of course bees too can produce substitute queens.

Another phenomenon of social regulation among termites: with some species, when a colony is being formed, the population coming from the royal couple's first brood always produces a soldier (sometimes two), representative of a special caste. As soon as this first soldier is taken away, the colony almost always produces a new soldier in his place. If you put a soldier from another termitary in a colony before it has produced its first soldier, this generation produces no soldier of its own. So extirpation of the first soldier produces another, addition of a soldier inhibits soldier-production in the colony. (Castle and Light, *vide* Grassé, 1949.)

The colony of termites functions as a unit. Every change in its composition leads to social regulation through larvae and nymphs being transformed. The society inclines towards a balance, keeping not only all castes, but a certain numerical balance of the castes. How is this achieved? Since the larvae, once they have reached the third stage, may come directly to sexual maturity (at any rate during a certain period of their lives), their development must normally be inhibited. Such an inhibition works in all parts of the colony, so it must be based on individual contact.

Biologists have looked for this contact in two different directions. One view is that the inhibiting influences are material that the royal couple emit, substances which are spread in the termitary by licking and mutual feeding, and which force the 'status quo' on individuals; similarly the soldier termites emit substances to stop larvae becoming soldiers, as they all could. The existence of something like 'socio-hormones' has been suggested, but so far there is no evidence for them at all. According to other biologists, the loss of the royal couple or of the first soldier alters the behaviour of the colony's members, so that new sensual stimuli are produced in their contacts with each other by

their altered behaviour. Such a hypothesis seems fairly plausible
after what we have seen of the effects of group stimulation on
swarming locusts.

Experiments carried out in 1951-2 by M. Lüscher show that
material influences do play a part in the normal inhibition of
larvae's sexual development: 'To decide which sort of inhibiting
effect was involved, a nest was built and divided into two parts by
a fine wire mesh wide enough for the insects to touch each other
through it quite easily with their antennae, but not wide enough
for them to pass matter through. Sexual forms with 20 larvae
from the same colony were put into Compartment A of the nest,
and in the other (Compartment B) only 20 larvae. Throughout
the experiment the insects touched each other very often through
the mesh. The orphaned colony in B developed as if they were
independent, producing substitute sexual forms—so contact by
antennae alone was not sufficient to stop this happening. In
one experiment, however, all the substitute sexual forms were
eliminated, and on new ones being produced they were also
eliminated, till the orphaned colony was so decimated that the
experiment had to be broken off. To release the elimination
mechanism, therefore, it was enough for the sexual forms in A
to register with their antennae the presence of substitutes in B.
The larvae in B kept on producing substitutes, however, although
registering with their *antennae* the presence of sexual forms in A;
so the fact that substitutes are prevented from appearing when true
sexual forms are present seems to depend not on sensory recognition by the larvae but on the true sexual forms emitting a material
inhibiting effect.'

*   *   *

We have already met the role of motion beside that of scent in
the communication of insects: ways of movement to give definite
directions. This brings us into the vast field of visual communications, of which many are familiar from domestic animals: the
expressions on the faces of cats and dogs, the movement of their
tails, their general posture, the position of horses' ears (and the

ears of other hooved animals). We know of birds' crests, ruffs and back-feathers bristling, and the way in which the crow family ruffle the whole of their plumage on head and neck. Through the penetrating observations of recent behaviour research we are gradually beginning to grasp the meaning of all these communications in their most subtle variants; we are learning, in fact, to transfer a few first words of these 'animal languages' into the language of our own thinking (Plate 14).

With these visual organs of communication the ascent to higher levels of differentiation can be seen very clearly. It is practically certain that hair and plumage have developed in connection with the fixing of a relatively stable body temperature —with the evolution of warm-blooded animals, that is, and with the amazing dispositions whereby the Emperor Penguin in the snow storms of the Antarctic, with the temperature nearly 100° Fahrenheit below freezing point and nature completely hostile to life, can keep a body temperature of about 100° Fahrenheit.

The growth of hair and plumage, and their development to this power of regulating body temperature, are among the dark unsolved problems of evolutionary research; we learn nothing about them even from the evidence of geology. But the transformation we see within the group of warm-blooded animals, in which hair and plumage change their function to become organs of social communication, is equally astonishing and mysterious. The muscles which make them bristle or smooth them down, the nerves which make such reactions possible, were all originally used to help the animal conserve heat; colouring and shape were unobtrusive and relatively indifferent to external view. But now, under the influence of changed inner circumstances, we see hair and plumage being used in specific reactions, either standing up or sleek; and these reactions are sometimes limited to a particular zone like head and neck or spine or anus. We can show how, hand in hand with this, the preferred zones can be picked out by the fact that the hair or plumage there is longer, or a more complex texture, more colourful or differently marked (Plate 17).

To say 'hand in hand' is perhaps unwarranted, for the hair and plumage may have remained in its original form when first expressing the internal change, the distinction of shape and colour coming only much later as a new stage. Or it could be the other way round, the differentiation of shape and colour coming first, and later being used to communicate inner conditions. The ways of development are innumerable, and many variants have come about in the course of evolution, so on this point we should be wise to suspend judgment (Figs. 10 to 12).

The way the external appearance becomes an organ of social communication goes with a great advance in brain development. The adaptation of display marks to new sets of functions, the new use of coat, muscles and nerves, takes place through new connections in the central nervous system. It is understandable, therefore, that with the evolution of the brain to a special level the social role of appearance can also reach a new level—as we can see from the example of the giraffe.

It used to be thought that the markings of giraffe and zebra had the function of dissolving the body's outlines and thereby giving protective colouring. But Theodore Roosevelt, who was an excellent observer as well as a huntsman, showed (in 1910) that the giraffe's markings gave no protective colouring, but on the contrary ensured that it would be easily seen. 'It is one of the most conspicuous animals in nature. Native huntsmen of the true hunter stock will always discover it from astonishing distances, and at close quarters their eyes never miss it.' Hediger satisfied himself by field studies that in their savanna habitat giraffes 'are in visual contact with each other over miles, and their conspicuous markings serve to control the relations of the individuals in a herd and also of the various herds with each other. . . .' (1949). Wherever it stands or goes the giraffe's markings are a signal of its presence, a delineation of its territory; and of course its exceptional shape is one of the many factors contributing to a general optical effect. Hediger stresses that the giraffe has remarkably few sebaceous (fatty) glands for a hoofed

FIG. 10. Variants of expression in a wolf's head. Above, left: leading wolf.
Right: middle-ranking wolf (gaze not so steady, ears going back). Centre
left: threat (rigid gaze, large pupils, swelling of brows and back of nose).
Right: apprehensive humility. Below, left: readiness for flight (back of nose
flat, forehead swollen). Right: suspicion and inclination to resist.

a   b

FIG. 11. Wolves' anal 'face'. Left: normal position. Right: expression of
superior wolf in 'social intercourse' (after R. Schenkel, 1947).

animal; to which we may add that an analysis of its brain formation shows the highest development of nervous centre among
artiodactyls (cloven-hoofed animals): the index of its cerebrum
is 29·5 compared with 20 in wild cattle and 14 in pigs.

b

FIG. 12. Possibilities of expression in back and tail. Above: peaceful position.
Below: bristling of the hair in threat (after R. Schenkel, 1947).

Many primate groups show the same evolution, in general structure and in developing a very effective optical means of communication. Long-tailed monkeys and baboons have highly developed brains, show striking facial colouring and marking of the anal zone in shape as well as colour, with a wide variety of gestures and postures, in which the tail plays a big part: the sexual importance of the anal zone is of course, since Freud, almost a commonplace. Such primate groups use smell much less as a means of communication.

The way the acoustic sphere has developed among vertebrates as means of communication is most remarkable, and we can luckily follow it at least in some stages, thanks to comparative studies of the internal organisation of the sense of hearing. A tiny part of the labyrinth, the organ originally adapted to our sense of balance, has been transformed to an acoustic organ. A small area of sensory cells has thus had assigned to it a completely new sense, a new quality of active perception: it is certainly a mysterious business. So far no one has been able to say what changed in these cells and in the nerve pathways and centres belonging to them, so that sounds are now heard more consciously, not merely registered as unconscious stimuli controlling the balance.

The findings of comparative morphology and physiology here plunge us right into the secret of change. The organ of sight is completely developed in the simplest forms of vertebrate known today, so that there we are not confronted so directly with the riddle of transformation from seeing merely light and shade or vague colours to seeing shapes.

Vertebrates' acoustic apparatus also poses the problem of correspondence between vocal organs and hearing organs. Some fishes have the latter but not the former, and others have both; in fact we know today that in some places there is much more sound under water than we once thought. We also know that amphibians may have vocal organs the same as birds, mammals and some insects.

The organ of balance has been changed to one of hearing, and the air passages in birds and mammals have become sound-producers: a unique dual transformation which means a quite new instrument of social contact over and above those made possible by smell and sight. Sounds as means of social relationship: the young chimpanzee has 32 different sounds, the young gibbon has 9 that are clearly distinguishable for the human ear; the howling monkeys of the South and Central American forests have 15 to 20—and we are already familiar with the social significance of 9 of these. Even where the sound-forms seem more monotonous, thorough observation discovers significant fine variants: an American ground-squirrel has over 6 vocal expressions with the most subtle gradations between them. We are just beginning to penetrate the peculiarities of under-water communication by whales and dolphins: several sound-forms are known, and the relations between the creatures of a group are manifold.

Vocal communication as part of relations between birds needs no special discussion here, for no vocal system in the animal kingdom has been more thoroughly investigated and recorded. But it is worth mentioning that birds produce sounds with quite a different instrument and nerve arrangement from those used by mammals: not the larynx, but the region where the trachea forks into the bronchial tubes, is the place for forming sounds; and the air-sacs which extend from the lungs into that region form an important part of their vocal apparatus.

*　　　*　　　*

The higher vertebrates evolve, the more social relations they form, both by transmitting more social stimuli and by receiving more sense impressions connected with social life. In cases where an animal responds to 'situations', we must presume that it has a particular inner state, in order that certain processes in its environment should act as stimuli at all. Biological research today must concentrate, therefore, on how things appear to the animals, not what they actually are—which is a great change from the days a few decades back when biologists were supposed to reduce everything to physico-chemical laws. Here is an example of this change.

We observe how young song-birds give their parents very active help in feeding them by the familiar action of opening their beaks, which are very brightly coloured. Let us take the shining scarlet inside the young jackdaw's throat. No matter how this scarlet is produced, it acts as a colour stimulus for the parent jackdaw; and when this scarlet is edged by the white swelling of the beak the question of *how* the white is produced is again of secondary interest to the biologist, who is concerned with the relations between old and young bird; for him the decisive fact is that white here means a contrast and thus an additional colour stimulus. Not that research into these colours by physical and chemical methods is unimportant; but that is a different branch of biology from the social and behaviour research we are concerned with here. This is the exciting new approach of biology, which makes a change of outlook so essential and which leads to a new basic concept of the organism.

Biology has been immensely enriched and refreshed by this new attention to 'appearances', and what they mean to the animal. The generation of biologists growing up today can scarcely imagine the extent to which many aspects of external structure, not to mention behaviour, were disregarded in the first decades of the century, being considered mere curiosities. In 1921, when I tried to show in my study of dragonflies that such 'curiosities' were really among the essential subjects of research, nobody showed much interest. Zoologists were chiefly concerned to classify and describe animals in a fixed system, and behaviour was at best a means towards this, instead of the subject of intensive research, centre of a wide field, that it is today.

The night heron's three white neck feathers—once a mere mark helping to classify the species—has become celebrated through Konrad Lorenz' observations, showing that they are a means by which the heron can be recognised by its young.

Thanks to the fascinating investigations of Tinbergen and his colleagues, even the most theoretical biologists are deeply interested in the scarlet belly of the male stickleback; and the same importance is accorded, quite rightly, to the strange red spot at the bottom of the herring-gull's bill. Another such characteristic mark is to be seen in the claws of 'fiddler crabs'.

The males of *Uca*, a genus of crab which reaches a large size on the sandy beaches of warm seas, are distinguished by strong, asymmetrical claws, one remaining dwarf, the other outsize and usually marked by very lively and conspicuous colouring. These claws raise the question of the hereditary factors producing asymmetry, where symmetry is the almost universal rule. The problem of right and left is also involved, and these crabs may well crop up in a discussion of human right- and left-handedness.

We shall be concerned several more times with the strange expressions of social life among these crabs, so we must have a closer look at the way they live. They are daylight creatures, and inhabit the tidal zone between high and low water-mark. There they dig individual holes almost straight down till they reach dry sand. When the tide goes out, they come to the surface right by their holes and feed on the fine layer of mud which is renewed by every incoming tide. The sea pours this mud on to the beach so lavishly that a great many crabs can find their food here. Only the small claws are used for feeding, so the females eat with both claws, but the males only with their small one. If they are ever disturbed, they go back into their holes. When the sea is approaching, they get hold of a piece of surface mud and cut it to fit as a roof when going into their hole. They stay safely in their holes while the tide is in, and when they want to come out, they take away their roof bit by bit (Figs. 13 to 15).

At low tide, when they are 'on dry land', they move their huge claw up and down, just as if they were waving, during which their body adopts specific positions (varying somewhat between the species), often displaying other colour marks most strikingly on their legs. On the sunlit beach they look a little like traffic

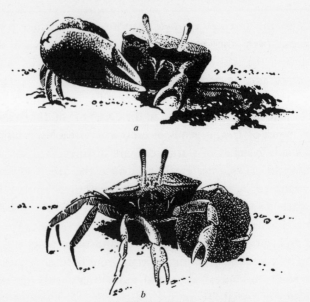

FIGS. 13a and 13b. Adult male fiddler-crab (*Uca latimanus*) feeding at low tide, for which he uses only the small left claw. Adult female of same species 'transporting' a ball of mud. Both claws are small and are used in feeding (after J. Crane, 1941).

FIG. 14. Male fiddler-crab (*Uca latimanus*). He has his white (sexual) colouring, whereas in Fig. 13a he is dark owing to change of mood (after J. Crane, 1941).

policemen directing the traffic with one huge glove—though as a matter of fact the small claw sometimes makes limited movements in rhythm with the larger one. At times the waving may occur at quite regular intervals of one to two seconds.

There are different views as to its function. Some think it is a relatively long-distance signal to keep off rivals from the area round the home hole. Others see it as exclusively a courting gesture during the mating season. One of the most recent studies of the genus *Uca* was made by Miss Jocelyn Crane (published in 1941), who watched the behaviour of twelve species on the same stretch of coast (in Panama). Her conclusion was that the truth lay somewhere between the two opinions. 'Waving, as in other crabs, is certainly carried on some of the time as a warning to

FIG. 15. Waving male crab (*Uca stenodactyla*). With this species the left claw is the big one and does the waving. Comparison with Fig. 14 also shows the difference in claw shape.

other males and to delimit territory in some (but not in all) species of *Uca*. On the other hand, in many, if not in all species, waving definitely plays a large part in courtship, and in one species at least (*latimanus*) is apparently carried on only by courting males.' Miss Crane also showed that the twelve different species were most strikingly distinguished in their waving by different shape and colour of the claws and different movements and postures.

So—through hundreds and thousands of structures and move-ments, scents and sounds, creature speaks to creature, to members of the species, to enemies, sometimes even to 'friends' from other species. All that speaks and is seen, heard, smelt or otherwise

'comprehended', can create significant relationships between one
life centre and another—whether the 'comprehension' is innate
and unconscious or acquired and decided by experience. The
most superficial and external features may illuminate our knowledge of the whole animal and his changing inner condition
(Plates 17 to 19).

*   *   *

If we compare the way vertebrate animals and human beings
express themselves, the common points are obvious. Our larynx
too produces sounds, our motor nerves allow us to make gestures,
our face muscles and the pupils of our eyes can also 'speak'.
Our tear-ducts are used in expression, our sweat-glands respond
to situations by sweat breaking out, our skin capillaries by
blushing and turning pale. Man too, in extreme cases, may
urinate, defaecate and vomit, as the violent expression of inner
states.

But the enumeration of agreements has already led to 'border-
line' situations where the animal-like organs in man are found
serving new and purely human functions. Our skin capillaries,
for instance, work not only in conditions which occur with
animals, such as rage or terror, but from the feeling of shame.
It is doubtful whether animals have anything like blushing for
shame; nor anything like smiling in amusement or affection.
Our language and certain conventional gestures also seem
specifically human, and outside the range of animal potentialities.

This uniqueness in human means of communication depends
on man's 'open-mindedness' and consequent freedom of decision.
We can turn our attention and interest to any object we choose,
whereas animals are limited to things which belong to the fixed
functions of their lives. All animal communication is largely an
automatic and inevitable reaction to situations which the animal
has somehow 'grasped'—by a mysterious integration of its
immediate environment with its inner condition. This applies
even to the bees' map-drawing and map-reading in the 'waggle-
dance'. Man, on the other hand, can control his means of

Plate 13. Brooding colony of gannet. This bird related to the pelican gets its name of *Sula bassana* from a famous Scottish brooding place, the Bass Rocks at the entrance to the Firth of Forth.   *Photo: Eric Hosking.*

Plate 14. Newly-fledged young horn-owl *(Bubo bubo)* in mounting excitement. Every feather is not only a heat-preserver and part of the characteristic pattern of the species, but also an organ expressing change of mood. Here all the feathers are already rising a bit and increase the bird's dimensions. Soon he will spread his feathers and adopt his most threatening position. *Photo: Elsbeth Siegrist.*

communication, and in human society, of course, often has to suppress them: in general we try to overcome expressions of pain, we prefer not to blush, and only laugh or cry if the conventions of our society approve of laughter and tears. We also learn to put on smiles like a sort of mask, which in turn are intended to produce a social mood-response in others.

As to human speech even psychologists and philosophers sometimes miss its central position as man's special distinguishing mark. Their theories still veer between two extremes: that speech is an instrument of social contact man has gradually developed, a late product in the evolution of an 'animal form' which was already human; or as a primary distinguishing-mark of man, since only with speech could man have his specific way of thinking and open-mindedness. Natural scientists have an understandable tendency to underrate human speech even more, since they almost always relate it to animal origins. But however much the organisation of larynx and nerves may correspond in man and in vertebrates, that explains very little about the phenomenon of speech in all its connections and effects; and when we talk of man at all, we always think of *speaking* man, so central is this function to our direct understanding of our environment, our special kind of intelligence and experience.

5

Instinct

THE WORD 'INSTINCT' (from the Latin *instinctus*, participle of *instinguere*, to incite) has fallen into disrepute, and many biologists avoid it even when the facts seem to call for its use. The reason why they do so will help towards an analysis of these facts.

The word has been in use for about two thousand years, and came into biological research overcharged with different meanings. Sometimes it means everything innate and unchangeable in a species as contrasted with whatever faculties individual animals and human beings might acquire in action; but sometimes these latter were also regarded (following Lamarck) as having become innate and 'instinctive' with the passage of time. It is no disparagement of Lamarck's great work in his day towards establishing the very idea of evolution, to say that his interpretation of development is no longer fruitful today.

Again, some scientists have used 'instinct' purely descriptively for behaviour performed with marked regularity by all the individuals of a species, as compared with the degrees of adaptation shown by perceptive behaviour; while others have thought of an inner drive or compulsion towards some particular objective, often defining 'instinctive' behaviour by reference to such a drive. But there were contradictions here too, for some regarded the objective as being the preservation of the species (since 'instincts' almost always contributed to this), while others thought of the objective as being something short-term and direct (like finding food, warmth, etc.), of course these two kinds of objective characterise completely different complexes of phenomena, and they have been strictly separated in modern behaviour research.

There was a further ambiguity in the use of the word 'instinct' which made it thoroughly unreliable. To understand this, we must go back to an earlier definition, according to which behaviour was instinctive if it was

(1) innate, not learnt;

(2) not individual but typical of the species, 'specific';

(3) performed with extreme regularity by the individuals of a species;

(4) helped to preserve the species.

Now, since experimental methods have come into their own, it has been noticed again and again that the processes in the embryo which bring about individual development are on exactly the same lines as the above definition of instinct. If we try to describe the forming of an eye from the first invisible structure in the embryo to the formation of the socket of the eye, the growth of the corresponding lens from outside, and finally of the nerve fibres, the process is parallelled point for point by the marks of instinctive behaviour. We could easily conclude that the way the animal comes into being also belongs to the realm of instinct, could speak loosely of 'instinct being at work', and then talk of 'development instincts' as a special class of impulses.

Of course processes of development and ways of behaviour do run parallel to quite a large extent in all forms of life, but when they became confused by such terminology, it made biologists still more suspicious of the very word 'instinct'. There were strange consequences of the confusion, for instance, in human biology. While psychologists were investigating the unconscious and the power of latent impulses, sociologists and ethnologists were showing how different civilisations had similar forms of expression; and these similarities were accordingly regarded as being deeply grounded in the human being's innate structure. Human instincts were classified (by von Monakow and Mourgue in 1930) as

(1) formative,

(2) those preserving the individual,

(3) sexual (preserving the species),

(4) social

        (all of which Man shared with animals);

and (5) religious, possessed only by man. Whereas for Fabre instinct had been the factor contrasted with human behaviour, one of the chief ways the animal organism could relate to its surroundings, in the first decades of our century the word became practically synonymous with life itself. After about 1930 the value of such a concept was subjected to a general reassessment.

*   *   *

As a result biologists became unwilling to call any animal behaviour instinctive. It was recognised that all behaviour was made up of many different components, some fixed and automatic, others highly adaptable and more or less modifiable by experience—like a mosaic where some of the pieces can be replaced by others without destroying the pattern.

For instance, there are all the movements and gland functions firmly fixed by innate structures, many of which may still be carried out when the highest nerve centres have been removed. Flying, swimming, walking, climbing, etc., are so automatic that they are sometimes called 'reflexes', though for modern neurologists 'reflex' does not imply an absolutely fixed response to a particular stimulus. It is short-hand for a response which is regular to a very high degree but may still be slightly modified by the actual processes of life.

Besides such almost automatic behaviour, all animals make a great many movements which are governed by external factors, such as attraction to or aversion from light, attraction to currents of air or water, to definite chemical stimulants, the search for contact with flat surfaces or corners (which are found by tactile stimuli). Biologists use the terms 'taxis' and 'tropism' for such reactions (e.g. phototaxis, phototropism, and rheotaxis, rheotropism for reactions to light and currents respectively), which may be more or less compulsive: i.e. an observer can predict them with some certainty under particular conditions. Each of these leads to a result important in the animal's life, to rest or food, sleep or reproduction, into light or shade, to or from humidity etc. The botanist, of course, finds taxes and tropisms very satisfactory, and they will also work for much of the activity of protozoa, for polyps, jellyfish, worms and other lowly creatures. But they will be used with less confidence where an animal is known to have a complex inner life, even if this has not been investigated in detail, because it is clear such an animal cannot be governed exclusively by a few simple environmental factors like humidity, warmth, light, current, etc.

Grassé, in his excellent study of termites' swarming, could present many details of this phenomenon, so important for the founding of new colonies, as relatively simple processes governed by external factors. Through this study we now know that the winged sexual forms of *Calotermes flavicollis* in Southern Europe need a relative humidity of about 50 or 70% to make them swarm, whereas those of *Reticulitermes* never swarm when it is under 65%. Humidity is also one of the reasons why the same termites in different climates may swarm at very different times of year; and a particular shower of rain may lead to swarming.

Again, whereas the larvae and 'neuters' in the termitary shun the light, the swarming sexual forms do the opposite: if they are day-time creatures, they seek the sunlight (which they have never seen before becoming mature); if they are night creatures they collect in thousands round a lamp. This attraction to light develops with the forming of properly functioning eyes, whereas before maturity, like all larvae, they have very little in the way of eyes.

But if at one stage of development the insect reacts to an external stimulus in one way, and at another stage in exactly the opposite way, the research worker cannot help realising that there is an internal change which in the last resort decides such reactions —so that Grassé too was led to discuss 'impulsions' and internal factors.

Moreover, even if the swarming of termites can be analysed in some depth in terms of reflexes and taxes, this is impossible when describing similar phenomena among higher animal forms, such as bird migration—although here too an important part is, of course, played by very simple environmental factors. We know, however, that the internal cause is more complicated, and accordingly harder to formulate in words. Grassé's study, in fact, shows up very clearly how much terminology is limited even for describing insect behaviour.

*   *   *

Insect behaviour is often supposed to be innate, rigid, un-changeable, the classic example of what was once called instinc-tive. But in fact parts of it may be quite plastic, as von Frisch showed in his remarkable studies of bee colonies (1952-53), based in turn on the pioneer work of C. A. Roesch.

Roesch found that although each worker bee can undertake all duties, they follow a definite time sequence in this, so that at a given age each bee will perform the same specific functions. There are three periods in their lives, during which particular glands also develop: pharyngeal glands in the first period, when they are engaged in feeding the larvae; wax glands in the second, when they are building the comb; and both of these atrophy in the third, when the bees are active only in the field, 'foraging'. Roesch describes their activities in more detail as follows:

'During the first two days of their life the bees clean out the cells from which workers have recently emerged, and coat them with a secretion of unknown kind and significance; only after a cell has been thus cleaned will the queen lay a new egg in it. There are a good many breaks from work, during which the bees either remain idle or collect on the brood-cells to keep them warm. On the third day they begin to feed the older larvae with honey and pollen. By taking in a great deal of pollen they bring their pharyngeal glands to such development that from the fifth day they produce enough food to feed the younger larvae. Their nursing activity is now at its height. It gradually abates during the second period at the same time as the pharyngeal glands subside.

'The activities of the second period (from about the tenth to the twentieth day) may occur in less strict time sequence. This period is characterised by the occupations which already take them out of the hive for a short while. In reconnaissance flights the young bees get to know the position of the hive and its environment. Dead bees and rubbish are removed. Inside the hive at this age they do whatever comb-building may be required and attend to the pollen brought in by the foragers. At the end of this period they may take on the function of guarding the hive entrance.

'From about their twentieth day to the end of their lives they are engaged solely in foraging for nectar, pollen and water. It is a very practical arrangement that the most dangerous "service" is taken over as the last of their functions.'

According to this description parts of the sequence may be changed. In a rather dramatic experiment Roesch put his bees into a situation in which the right worker class was not available for urgently necessary duties. He partitioned off an observation-hive with over a thousand numbered bees of a known age, having first driven them all into compartment A and turned it round an angle of 180°. The young bees, which had not yet flown out, naturally remained in A; later, on leaving the hive, they took their bearings from the new entrance on this side. The older bees left the hive without taking bearings, and on returning home took the familiar way, which now led them into compartment B. The hive was thus divided into 'young folk' in A and 'old folk' in B. There were no foragers in A, stores were quickly used up, and some of the inhabitants were already lying starving on the ground, when suddenly young bees flew out to forage, which according to their age and their fully developed pharyngeal glands were still brood-nurses. They remained in the field foraging, and the feeding glands degenerated in a few days. In B there were no nursing bees; but the young larvae were looked after all the same, and the worker bees kept fully developed pharyngeal glands up to an age of four weeks. In another experiment when most of the building workers were removed from a hive, the old bees' wax glands were regenerated, and the combs needed were built.

So the bees' activity at a given age is not decided only by the morphological development of their glands. It may be the other way round, such development being influenced by the needs of the hive. To what extent this actually happens and how it comes about, is a problem of the future.

From these experiments it is clear that the system Roesch originally suggested for division of labour may be greatly modified under abnormal conditions; what about normal ones? Lindauer confirmed the system in general, but found that some details of the sequence were very flexible. The cleaning of cells does come at the beginning of all duties, but it may be carried on over weeks, without clear limits, alongside other activities. In his observations young and old larvae were nursed interchangeably without any apparent rule. Nursing of brood and building could go on together over several weeks. Two-day-old bees were sometimes found secreting wax and building. Of 159 bees observed until and including 'field service' 136 jumped their 'guard duties', while of the remainder 23 carried these duties out much longer than usual, one for 9 successive days, till she was killed in a battle with a wasp.

It is remarkable how long they are not working at all. Bee No. 107, for instance, which was observed continuously from the first day of her life, in the 20 days of her duties in the hive, up till her first foraging flight, worked only 50 hours of the 139 during which she was observed and spent the remaining 89 'at leisure'. Of these 89 she sat still for $39\frac{1}{2}$, and for $49\frac{1}{2}$ marched slowly and at ease round the combs, now cursorily inspecting a cell, now making brief contact with a neighbour. There are a great many such patrolling idlers, which, as Lindauer pointed out, is one reason why reserves are quickly available where they are needed for a particular duty. The time for developing feeding glands and wax glands varied among his bees even under normal conditions more than had been supposed till then, which obviously meant that there were more suitable variants for an abnormal demand than Roesch's system envisaged. In the light of this many of the rules for bees' co-operation become easier to understand.

The deeper we penetrate into insect life, the clearer we see here too that individuality so vital to our understanding of the animal kingdom. For a further example of how the rigid side of insect behaviour may be relaxed, I quote from von Frisch:

'Roesch (1925) thought that when bees start foraging they first look for a source of food independently and only later learn to understand the dances whereby older foragers inform the hive of a rewarding harvest. That was certainly a mistake. There are scouts which look for new sources independently, and harvesters which fetch the crop from an already known source. A scout which has found a good crop goes on exploiting it and becomes a harvester. The overwhelming majority of worker bees, however, never act as scouts, but follow the dances of their hive members pointing to a particular objective. Only a few are pioneers; the mass go where they are skilfully directed—one of the many parallels between bee-hives and human society. Within the final period of their lives the scouting is not tied to a particular age. The scouts are often inexperienced bees flying out to harvest for the first time; but they are often old, experienced harvesters, discovering independently a new kind of blossom when those visited till then have no more yield. Even among these old bees there are great individual differences. Most of them stay at home when their food source dries up, waiting for new instructions. Few are resourceful enough to discover a replacement quickly.

'What I have just reported is the result of observations over several years by Therese zu Oettingen-Spielberg (1949). To be able to watch the behaviour of all scouts and gatherers, she put her observation bees in a big apiary shut off from the outside world by a wire mesh. The surprisingly small number of scouts is best seen from the fact that in her experiments, though hundreds of bees flew out and swarmed round the room, only three per hour (at an average worked out over 54 hours of observation) discovered any of the abundant flowers bearing nectar or pollen which were available. It might be thought that the unnatural conditions of a limited flying space gave a false impression of the bees' behaviour; but in the summer of 1949 Lindauer was able to confirm the result by another method with bees flying at large (still unpublished). Of 159 numbered bees, whose transition from duties inside the hive to duties outside could be continuously observed, 150 were directed to these duties by the dances of other bees and only 9 flew out foraging on their own accord.'

Is this distinction in the activities of foraging bees a further 'specialisation', or does it include a moment of 'freedom'? This latter possibility is hinted at by von Frisch, who points out an equally unexpected division among foragers. 'Anyone who has watched these dances in many colonies and with thousands of individuals, must marvel at the extraordinary, always recurring precision of the action. But he will also recognise with amazement that these insects, however much innately tied to the fixed traditions of their species, have yet kept a degree of individual freedom, which alone makes this intricate system practical and adaptable. When, for instance, a quarter of a mile south of the hive a luxuriant source of nectar has been discovered, when dozens of dancing bees point in that direction and to that distance, and hundreds of "novices" set out to forage round that area, there will always be some who go miles further away or forage right by the hive. Have they not understood the "language"? Whatever the cause of their "deviation", seen in the context of the whole hive, they are very useful eccentrics. For if there is a field of rape-seed blooming in the south, it is a good idea not only to make the most of this but to keep a look-out in case it begins to bloom in the north or east or at a different distance away. The familiar loyalty of bees to a blossom is always offset by exceptions to the rule. It just happens that even in this respect bees are individually different; some are true to one kind of blossom and go on gathering there even as the nectar dries up, after which they stay at home inactive, waiting for better times; while others, less common, leave their blossom at the slightest provocation and keep a look-out somewhere else in case there is a better store.

'In the same way it is biologically sensible that the great mass of "rising generation", on attaining the age of foragers, should collect on the "dancing floor" and there wait for directions as to where their forces are most urgently needed at the time. In spring, where there are large colonies, hundreds are available every day as new foragers; and it would be uneconomical if they all flew off foraging independently. But they would also be all condemned to inactivity, if there were not also the few "deviators", the resourceful and adventurous bees who go their own way.

'It is the same with the whole division of labour. Only deviation from the system, the flexibility of the individual, offers a guarantee of harmony in the hive—even when the system is disturbed by external conditions, as is continually happening.'

* * *

Bees, then, are highly adaptable to changing conditions, altering both structure and behaviour where the state of the hive call for it. But this plasticity is not confined to extremely 'social' insects like bees; it is shown equally by the sand-wasp *Ammophila*, whose social behaviour is so much simpler than the bees'.

As we have seen in an earlier chapter, *Ammophila* works on several nests at once and can divide her time satisfactorily between her different activities through 'unladen visits', which are really inspections. Normally, if a nest has a larva in it, waiting for food, the wasp will go off to fetch the food. But when Baerends removed the larva before the inspection, or replaced it with a dead one, the wasp would inspect, then give up the nest for good and turn to work on other nests. Similarly, if a wasp finds an egg in a nest she is inspecting, she will not bring it any more food; but when Baerends replaced the egg before inspection with a larva, the wasp made her inspection, and at once started supplying food regularly. So these inspections really influence her behaviour, she does not just continue automatically with actions which have become pointless. The state of the nest is registered, and has its effects.

But we must beware of sweeping conclusions. For if *Ammophila* is subjected to such tests while seeing to the feeding of the larva, i.e. *after* the inspection, the result is quite different. If the larva she found in the nest before, is taken away, she will go on bringing food without hesitation. If an egg is brought into the nest instead of a larva, she will go on supplying caterpillars, as if there were a larva there busy eating. So in the phase of getting food, the visits to the nest are completely different in character from the 'unladen visits'. In the former she shows herself a relative 'automaton', as she has sometimes been considered, by going on with actions which no longer fit the new situation; in the latter she is somehow affected by a new inner condition, so that she registers a nest's particular state and gathers impressions (which soon afterwards she can no longer do, once she is at her usual food-bringing). These short phases of increased adaptability are built into the whole way in which she looks after her brood; they have an important place in an ordered course of events. In these brief moments, as illustrated in her whole behaviour, she comes specially near to the higher animals. I cannot resist quoting Baerends' report on a particular wasp, known from its marking as 000, with which he experimented very intensively for about three weeks:—

'On 24th July, 1940, 000 completes the first stage of Nest 61; on 25th she opens Nest 68 (unknown to me till then) and brings food here later. When I am putting in a plaster nest here, I find the young larva with its first caterpillar. It seems to me not quite healthy, and I find that the wasp, after her next unladen visit, has stopped looking after the nest. On 26th she inspects Nest 61, but the larva has not yet emerged (A). On 28th she digs Nest 84; when she arrives there with her first caterpillar, I have a caterpillar in there for her. She throws out the strange caterpillar, puts her own in, and lays an egg on it (B). On 30th she again inspects Nest 61; I have previously replaced its contents with a cocoon.

She closes the nest, and I do not see her there again (C). Now she begins to dig Nest 356, but does not supply it with food till 2nd August, because the weather in the two days between is very bad. On that day she also visits Nest 84, but the larva here has not yet emerged. So she brings no food here (D), but builds a new nest, which, however, is destroyed by me in trying to replace it with a plaster nest. On 3rd August she again visits Nest 84, into which I have previously brought six caterpillars. She then closes the nest (probably for good, but this I cannot say for certain) and stops bringing food here (E). On 4th she works first on the first stage of Nest 340, and finishes this stage; later she comes to inspect Nest 365 and then takes a caterpillar there as food. On 5th she digs Nest 423, brings the first caterpillar there and lays an egg on it. Then she inspects Nest 356 in its third stage. Before she brings a caterpillar there, I replace the larva with a caterpillar and egg; she brings in her caterpillar, without letting herself be disturbed by the larva's absence (F). After an hour, however, she makes an inspection here. There being no larva in the nest, she stops bringing food here (G). The contents of the nest afterwards rot from the rain. On 6th she opens Nests 340 and 423; the eggs have not yet been hatched, and she stops bringing food here (H and I), but digs a new nest 440. From 7th to 14th the weather is very bad, and it is not till 14th that she starts on the third stage of Nest 423. On 16th I take the larva out of the nest, and she makes an inspecting visit, after which she closes it for good, without there being a larva in the nest (J). Then she begins on the second stage of Nest 440—and I give up my observations of her.

'Although, therefore, this wasp has been disturbed in many ways, she has always reacted "logically" both to the nest's natural content and to its content as altered by me' (Fig 16).

To this flexible behaviour we may add the complicated powers of orientation which such wasps have been observed to show (by Baerends with *Ammophila*, by Tinbergen and his colleagues with *Philanthus*, the so-called bee-moth). W. H. Thorpe, discussing perceptive learning among invertebrates (1950), writes as follows:—

'Nobody who has experimented with these insects can help

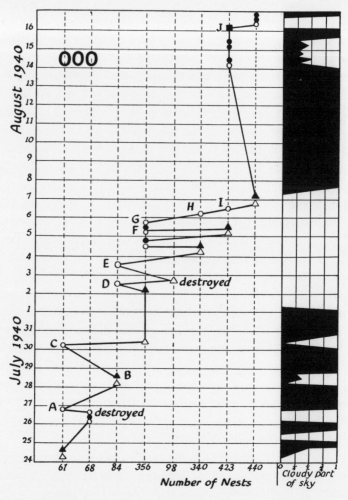

FIG. 16. Diagram of activity of sand-wasp 000 from 24th July to 16th August, 1940. The code is explained in Fig. 7; all important details in text. The black on the right shows the cloudy parts of the sky: the increased activity on cloudless days (26th July, 14th and 15th August) is striking. Such a diagram gives some idea how much the wasp's success in rearing depends on the weather (after Baerends, 1941).

feeling amazed at the thorough knowledge they seem to possess of the nest environment. When they have got a prey which is to be brought into the nest, they can easily be caught and moved about thirty yards away in a dark box. As soon as they are free again, they generally set out at once, without any hesitation, on the right way to the nest, unperturbed by obstacles, and find a well-camouflaged burrow which our eyes could not detect, and even if they could, would not find again without special markings. From these investigations we are obliged to conclude that there is a fundamental similarity between these insects' behaviour and the way we find our bearings with the aid of landmarks. It is a problem for the neurologist that the insect brain can function like this, having no structures comparable with the maze of a mammal's cortex.'

New evidence on the different behaviour of individual insects has been produced by G. D. Shafer's study of the American mortar-wasps *Sceliphron cementarium* and *Chalybion coerulium*, both of which prey on spiders as food for their larvae. This highly illuminating study is in many ways supplementary to Baerends' work. One interesting point it reveals is that the wasps have long rest periods in between looking after their brood, which is here complicated by the walls of the mortar-comb. Shafer notes too an 'inspection ceremony' as occurring with the species he observed, and gives examples of their adapting to altered situations at greatly varying speeds. He is also the author of a charming little book wholly concerned with a disabled wasp, 'Crumplewing'; by feeding her and providing caterpillars when it was clear she could not fly, he helped her to carry out her 'daily duties'.

*   *   *

The analysis of what used to be generalised as instinctive behaviour has of course led scientists to try to classify more exactly the component parts of such behaviour. As this is a field of research where the theoretical framework is being very thoroughly transformed, we cannot expect any final results. It is more in the stage of blue-prints submitted by several architects for a public building to be designed; so a brief survey here is only intended to show the most important new developments.

In 1918 Craig made an illuminating distinction, which was only given full validity by Lorenz some twenty years later: the innate and fixed processes in animal behaviour were distinguished from 'appetitive behaviour', where the animal was driven to satisfy a particular drive. Besides the appetites for food and drink, there are sexual appetites, those for social life, for looking after young, and for states of rest, such as sleep—even sleepiness is thus a special form of appetitive behaviour.

The other processes, as has been said, are innate in the animal's structure and have become almost automatic. Once the animal has found food and swallowed it, the disposal of that food is fixed by innate rules; and other animal actions are fixed in the same way. When an animal has found a sexual partner, brood to be nursed, a member of the same social group, a place of rest, the further course of its behaviour is based on innate co-ordination which is relatively fixed. Lorenz called this part 'instinct' to give the word a more limited use and save it from being completely abandoned.

Appetitive behaviour, i.e. the observable consequence of an inner condition, varies from one group of animals to another, and shows particularly striking differences between higher and lower levels of differentiation. Two extreme variants are possible: either such behaviour starts in the attempt to satisfy a drive, and in the course of time is determined by individual experiences (as is very often the case with man); or it is largely fixed by innate adjustment to stimuli in the environment, such as definite scents, light, darkness, a closely limited range of preferred temperatures, the touching of smooth or rough, hard or soft surfaces.

These attractions or taxes may be bound up with complicated actions, and many of them play an important part in the human organism: For instance, whenever we look at something, the object is focused on the appropriate place of our retina, without our

Plate 15. A group of sea-elephants have made their quarters in an extensive penguin colony. Half-way between New Zealand and the Antarctic the island of Marquarie rises out of the ocean, scarcely three miles wide at its widest point. Seals, sea-elephants and penguins come here year after year to reproduce on land.   *Photo: Norman Laird,* National Geographic Magazine.

Plate 16. Sea-elephants *(Mirounga leonina)*. *Photo: J. Sapin-Jaloustre, French Polar Expeditions.*

Plate 17. The male sage grouse *(Centrocercus urophasianus),* an American relative of the European hazel grouse, changes his appearance very drastically in courting display, especially in the frontal aspect which is presented to the hen. In the white breast-feathers two bare patches of skin are blown up to orange-yellow balls through air-sacs lying underneath.

Photo: C. W. Schwarz, Natural History, *New York.*

Plate 18. Climax of courting ritual by sage grouse: the head has completely vanished in the crop-feathers. The neck-sacs on contraction of the muscle produce a sound which (when there is no wind) can be heard a mile away. These American birds have regular places where at dawn and dusk the old cocks occupy their territories and carry out their ceremonies. Observers report from 11 to 450 cocks at one courting place between March and June.

Photo: J. van Wormer, Audubon Magazine.

being aware of it: the retina in a vertebrate's eye is among other things an automatic view-finder (Koehler, 1950).

Our human taxes almost all work in the unconscious sphere: e.g. the many stimuli to our labyrinth from the earth's gravity, and the sense organs inside the body which make their reports on the position of the muscles to the control station in the unconscious. There will, of course, be many conscious factors slightly altering the course of taxes, just as there are many unconscious factors present in acquired skills. There are no hard and fast boundaries in this field; and Hinde (following up his studies of the great tit quoted in an earlier chapter) gives many examples in a later work (1953) to show that there is only a difference of degree, not of kind, between appetitive behaviour and 'instinct', in Lorenz' sense of innate co-ordination. He recognises, however, that Lorenz' division may be very useful in many cases.

* * *

At this point we might look at a phenomenon much remarked on by biologists in the last decade, though so far little investigated. As far back as 1911 Heinroth observed that young geese which do not see their parents on being hatched will take man as a parent and follow him just as they would a real parent. Lorenz showed that it only needed a short time after they came out of the egg, in some cases only a few minutes, to tie the gosling for life to Man as foster-parent—first Man in general, and perhaps later, through long habit, particular individuals. Lorenz pointed out the importance of this social bond, which is fixed for such a long time, even for life, and called the process 'imprinting'. It is a phenomenon which occurs in various forms with birds, fishes and even insects.

Interesting details have been produced by E. Fabricius, a Swedish ornithologist, who has recently studied the ducklings of several species. He first established the length of time during which the duckling may be susceptible to such imprints: their susceptibility is great for twelve hours after leaving the egg, and has receded entirely when they are twenty-four hours old. They react to a combination of optical and acoustic stimuli, the latter's effect lasting rather longer than the former's: a rhythmically repeated monosyllabic call together with a movement on the ground (a mechanical duck's swimming movement does not 'work'). Once the imprint is successful with these ducks, it is definitive. The phenomenon seems to be based on a very plastic innate faculty being realised, which develops by integrating the optical stimulus of particular movements with the acoustic stimulus of particular sounds.

W. M. Thorpe (1944) extends the working hypothesis of an 'imprint' which fixes social bonds, to the 'imprint' of surroundings which are seen as soon as the bird is hatched and so can perhaps be fixed as future hatching places.

We are far from knowing what really happens in 'imprinting', but this strange form of learning 'once-for-a-lifetime' is clearly a border-line between learning processes more extended in time and the innate co-ordination of instinctive behaviour: in fact, it shows us once again how close the latter is to appetitive behaviour, and the latent structural features common to all forms of experience.

*   *   *

The attempts to distinguish innate and acquirable components of animal behaviour show the great complexity of the facts. To illustrate the results of such analysis I will take the familiar phenomenon of young song-birds 'gaping' to beg for food, aided by the colour of their throats and the swelling of their bills, which we have already come across in another context. This example offers us a simple social relationship, and we also see how such a 'meeting' between parents and child is realised. I shall follow the investigations of Monika Holzapfel and also of Tinbergen and Kuenen, which were published independently of each other in 1939 and are complemented by H. Prechtl's study in 1953 and H. Wackernagel's morphological work.

The stretching out of the neck and opening of the coloured throat occur spontaneously, i.e. without demonstrable external stimulus, in the very first days of the bird's life. Later the spontaneous releases become less common, and external stimuli may be needed to release the 'gaping'. The eyes are still closed in the first period in the nest, and vibration stimuli, which may be produced by the parent bird flying off, are effective with thrushes nesting in the open. With birds like the starling which breed in the hollows of trees, contributory factors may be direct contact with the swelling of the bill, violent shaking of the nest and also acoustic stimuli; but vibration and attempts to produce optical stimuli are equally negative in result. With starlings the touch stimulus is the strongest of these releasers (Plates 20-22).

The response to such releasing stimuli is at first not directed: the chick strains its neck straight up in the air; the movement's orientation is opposed to gravity. To find the throat is up to the feeding parent bird.

As soon as the eye-lids open, a complex form of stimulus becomes a releaser instead of touch stimuli: experiments with models show that the chick gapes at a particular 'form', which always has three features: the releasing object must move, be over $\frac{1}{8}''$ in diameter, and be above the horizon of the nestlings' eyes; in normal life the parent bird's head is the releaser which produces this gaping. But it is not only the stimulus which changes with the growth of the young birds; their response also becomes different—for the gaping is now directed, its objective is plainly the parent bird's head. These two changes are the result of growth processes in the young bird which are fixed by heredity: the growing and forming of the vertebral column of the neck and its movement apparatus, the maturing and development of the sensory organs and the brain. These developments occur at different speeds, so that there is a transition stage where the visual stimuli are already working, but the response is still against gravity and straight up in the air, not yet directed at the parent's head.

The way this gaping matures in young songbirds is a chapter of behaviour research which brings many conclusions. During the first days in the nest the chick is too immature to take its bearings, which would result in a practical and independent behaviour, and the parent bird must maintain the natural 'course of events', by looking for the bill which the chick can just open. Even with open eyes, up till about the twelfth day, the starling chick is physically incapable of coming to meet the feeding head. The whole appetitive behaviour has become a real social act—an occurrence of great importance for our understanding of social development. The greater an animal's faculties, the longer it will take to reach maturity, and to give it time for this, the more and the longer the young animal's early appetitive behaviour will be based on subtle interaction with the parent animal's behaviour: interaction of two members of a species.

Let us stop a moment at this fact. The instinctive gaping is no good unless it is co-ordinated with an act of orientation towards the parent bird and unless the corresponding pattern of behaviour is an innate part of the parent bird's structure: The two forms of behaviour are complementary and continue to be complementary parallel with the stages in the chick's growth: this social quality is within the individual from birth, it does not grow up afterwards.

The observations of a gaping starling chick provide many details of interest. If we feed it with a brush dipped in food, to which it has become accustomed from the beginning, the brush turns into the parent bird. If after a fortnight we bring the brush near it, it will at once stretch its head towards the 'feeding brush' —so it can now make the movement in the right direction of its own accord. But as soon as it opens its beak and gapes, it is as if riveted to the spot by a magic spell, incapable of any movement or getting the food it has strained for. Even if we move the brush a few fractions of an inch in front of the chick's gaping bill, it will still be 'spell-bound': so the gaping is an innate special form of behaviour, in clear contrast with the later orientation behaviour. A few days later, from its 18th to its 20th days, shortly before it flies off, it will hop or flutter to meet the feeding brush. But even now it will remain spell-bound as soon as it begins to gape.

The starling later goes over to foraging for its own food (we had better not say it 'learns' to do this, because it has not yet been proved whether this is real 'learning' or the maturing of different innate behaviour). How complex the transition is, has been shown by Monika Holzapfel's experiments. Two groups of

FIG. 17. (a) With the Emperor penguin there is no need for nest-building, for the parent bird lays the egg on her powerful feet and keeps it warm by a special brooding fold in the skin of the belly. The chick, too, is looked after in the same way in its earliest days. (b) The old bird regurgitates food which the chick takes direct into the oral cavity. The interlocking of old and young bird is the reverse of that with most song-birds (from photographs taken by French polar expeditions).

starlings were continuously supplied with enough food until they were able to forage for themselves. When that time came, one group was fed only once a day with the brush, the other group every two hours. The birds left more 'to their own devices' stopped gaping many weeks earlier than the other group. In natural circumstances the parents first stop their feeding activities, which makes the childish behaviour stop sooner. So the stopping is not a completely fixed process but rather labile.

We have seen the unity of behaviour in old and young birds in a highly specialised group; other kinds of birds achieve this by their own particular means. The 'interaction' is different, for instance, with penguins, pelicans and their relatives. Whereas the parent song-bird puts the food into the chick's open throat, the young penguin looks for the beak of its parent bending down towards it, and sticks its bill deep in the parent's throat (Fig. 17). And the same social structure is realised with the most varied of methods.

The young bird's gaping is a typical 'instinct' in the limited sense which Lorenz gave to such a complex of innate co-ordination. What is often called the instinct of gaping almost always means more than that, because it includes the directing actions. But of course appetitive behaviour, as is obvious from this example, has very great similarities with actual instinct; and in separating the component parts of behaviour, we should never forget that they are part of a unified whole, which leads through the individual to the life of the species. They are like scattered accessible islands in an ocean we have set out to map and to traverse.

*   *   *

For a long time after Fabre's day his digger-wasps with their 'anatomical knowledge' used to stand as the great contrast in behaviour to Man, so deficient in instinct, so laboriously learning and seeking and training. The new attempts by biologists to analyse the forms of behaviour once simply called instinct, have shown that this was a rather vague and negative way of looking at human behaviour: we can now be a good deal more precise in our comparative judgment of it.

We should first note that the number of 'instincts' (in Lorenz' sense) which decide our relations to animate and inanimate environment, in fact our behaviour, is no smaller than with higher animals. The innate structures which allow our sensory organs to function, all the fixed taxes which are at work unconsciously, for instance, in our organs of balance and our eyes, play the same part with us as with our animal relatives. On the other hand, the structures by which environment is experienced, which function in appetitive behaviour, are completely transformed in their method of functioning by the special way we experience our environment. Our deficiency in instincts must be seen positively as a special 'freedom in direction', which distinguishes man in a decisive way from the norm of the higher animals.

6
Mood

LET US RETURN to the fiddler crabs on the sandy beaches of
Panama's west coast, as described by Miss Jocelyn Crane.
It will be remembered that they live in the zone of flat sand
left by the tide going out.

'A strong spirit of individuality was observed in the fiddler
crabs, and I agree with Pearse that some of their behaviour can
only be interpreted as sheer play. Several adjacent males of
similar size, belonging to the same species, on the same day would
show definite traits of individuality. One would be especially
belligerent, seeking every excuse for a duel, another would build a
shelter and display strenuously all day, scarcely stopping to feed,
the third, although he had spent most of the preceding day
fighting and courting, might on this morning feed continuously
and enlarge his burrow, punctuating his activity with only a few
half-hearted displays.

'Similarly some females of various species were much given
to wandering about, peering down the holes of adult males,
hurriedly retreating, paying brief and successive attention to the
displays of a number of neighbouring males, and altogether
behaving in a manner which in higher animals would certainly be
termed coy and flirtatious. I have used these ultra-anthropo-
morphic terms advisedly, because I have been unable to find any
other words in the language which so exactly define the activities
of these individual females. Others, of the same species, spent
hours feeding quietly in several square inches of ground. In the
end members of the latter group proved just as susceptible as the
wandering individuals to the advances of displaying males.

'Two large male *stylifera* furnished a good example of a social
relationship of sorts which continued for at least a week. Their

burrows were a yard apart, in an uncrowded portion of the beach, although other males of their own species were close by. Every day they followed an invariable routine, consisting of emergence, cleaning, feeding, accompanied by change to display coloration, and then—without a sign of preliminary waving or warning or argument of any kind—they would meet on the invisible boundary line between their burrows and fight. The duel always ended several minutes later in identical fashion, the smaller being somersaulted backward by the larger. The vanquished would then pick himself up and retreat hastily to his burrow, while the winner resumed feeding without another glance. After a half-hour or so more both would begin to display, without taking any further notice of each other. I never saw two fights on one day, and there was never any female in their vicinity. Finally both moved away and I lost track of them.

'One of the most individualistic, inexplicable performances I saw was that of a moderate-sized but apparently adult male *terpsichores*. His display coloration was not well developed on the day in question, his usually white carapace being heavily streaked with dull yellow and his cheliped scarcely pink. He did not build a hood or display, but enlarged his burrow and fed energetically. Then, suddenly, he went straight over to the newly erected shelter of a neighbour fully 18" away. Without any provocation or preliminaries he undermined the shelter from the rear and pushed it down on top of its owner; the two crabs then spent fifteen minutes fighting, in the course of which both darkened rapidly, losing all trace of display coloration, and the shelter owner lost the tip of his pollex. Finally the aggressor let the owner go, then went directly to the next hood, 6" from the first, and repeated the episode exactly. In this case, too, the owner was powerless and was constantly thrust down his own hole, although he put up a good fight. At last, after another 25 minutes of uninterrupted struggle, the aggressor released this crab also, and returned, without hesitation, to his first victim, who by now was cleaning himself up and had regained most of his display coloration. At the approach of his former antagonist, the victim tried to flee down his hole, but was seized from behind. Another duel, lasting no more than several minutes this time, followed, and ended as on the first two occasions with the aggressor's abruptly releasing his victim. This time the former returned slowly but directly to his own hole, cleaned himself and began to feed. Neither of the two victims rebuilt their shelters on that day, although the tide was only slightly past dead low at the time.

'The general conclusion to be drawn from all this variability of action is that fiddler crabs, nervously the most highly organised of all crustacea, show a truly remarkable latitude of behaviour.'

Here is something like ownership and defence of a territory, just as in the world of the dragonflies. Here is spontaneous aggressiveness: is it a general characteristic of the *Uca* male, or is it exclusively part of their sexual rivalry? Here is the urge for proximity to other members of the species, that most elementary social phenomenon. All these factors call for closer analysis, but for the moment we will concentrate on the male's changing of colour, which obviously plays an important part in the life of *Uca*.

The *Uca* females and the young of both sexes are in many species grey-brown and relatively inconspicuous, though some of them show livelier markings. In the early morning, when the sexually mature males come out of their channels, they also have this simple garb of their species. But when with the tide going out they have spent some time on dry land and in the sun, an amazing change sets in, colours and markings becoming most conspicuous. *Uca stylifera* turns dazzling white in its body; but the big claw, which is also mainly brownish when the crab first appears, develops a fine combination of bright chrome yellow in the bottom parts, glowing orange on the centre and brilliant white on the movable finger. Parts of the strutting legs become a gleaming scarlet. The whole blaze of colour may appear in a quarter of an hour, then persist all day in normal circumstances, and fade again towards evening. With *Uca latimanus*, another of the twelve species which are found on the beaches of Panama, the body also becomes pure white, but the big claw is orange at the base and white in the main part. The fronts of its strutting feet are streaked with purply red—like plums. This species, however, needs about two hours to change into its glowing courting dress.

If you were to catch one of these male crabs with the aim of painting him in all his glorious hues, you would be in for a disappointment, because the catching too affects his colour, which gradually begins to fade, and you would soon afterwards see only a brownish creature as inconspicuous as the females and the young. Even when the males fight during their courting, their hue turns brown after only a few minutes, and does not resume its splendour till the actual courting display begins.

In contrast to the cuttlefish, the fiddler crab's colour changes are not governed by nerves, as was once supposed. Since 1925 we have known through G. Koller's observations that they are caused by substances in the blood-stream, by hormones: various such substances work on the colour cells, so that the pigment either spreads rapidly or concentrates in the cell in the narrowest space. Further research then led to various hormone-forming glands being discovered, of which specially important ones are situated in the stalk of the eye (these crabs have compound-eyes which stand on long movable stalks). *Uca* has played an important part in such experiments; in fact the amount of colour-changing hormone is reckoned in *Uca* units, as with vertebrates it is reckoned in mouse and rat units. The effect of the eye-stalk hormone on *Uca*, incidentally, is the opposite of its effect on other crabs: it generally makes them lighter, but *Uca* darker. We are far from understanding the colour change in details; all we know is that it is governed by hormones—presumably several of them.

*   *   *

The hormones, however, are simply helping factors; there are other causes within the crab. For one thing the colour cells must be innately so disposed and distributed, that when definite substances circulate, the colour either sets in or disappears in the specific distribution: the colour cannot change unless a colour organ is ready to react. There is a second precondition, however, which must be considered 'central'. For the hormones are integrated into the fiddler crab's whole organism, and as we saw, the colour change is connected with what the crab does or has done to it. The secretion of hormones into the blood takes place in particular situations, is part of those situations. The change of colour leads us from the crab's appearance to the inner condition of a living creature, the modest centre of independent action in its small domain on the sunny beach.

The phrases 'living creature' and 'independent action' plunge us into the mystery of the individual animal which can *have* such an 'inner condition'. This last phrase is the safest for the un-known factors which we can deduce from exterior phenomena. It is static, and as behaviour very often involves motion, such a phrase may very easily be found unsatisfactory. More dynamic words, like 'drive' and 'urge' creep into our descriptions, taken involuntarily from the sphere of human experience and the language appropriate to that—since this is the only sphere from which fairly precise testimony on inner states can be given.

Language, indeed, raises a particular difficulty here, for many words and phrases in this sphere have nuances of meaning in different languages which are untranslatable: the German *Stimmung*, the French *humeur*, the English *mood*, though they may be roughly equivalent, are not exactly the same. But at least modern zoologists, since the 'thirties, whatever language they speak, have been at one in recognising the importance of animals' 'inner condition': it is stressed not only by imaginative and perhaps sentimental animal-lovers, but by the most precise and practical research workers who are most careful to avoid anthro-pomorphism and to describe only observable phenomena.

Parallel with this recognition has been the progressive dis-covery of the unconscious, which has helped towards a new valuation of the feelings in human life, so often underrated in comparison with the intellect. Both philosophy and psychology have come to realise the importance of 'moods' as determining the way Man experiences and reacts to his environment. A mood is not the subjective disturbance or distortion of a normal, neutral state, but the basis of a changing 'normality'. We all know of things we are only capable of doing when 'in the mood'. That mood will govern our feelings about ourselves and our environment when we are in it, and may also have physical effects—e.g. a mood of great misery may literally cause nausea. Now, however careful we must be in applying the contents of human experience to animals, it is evident that animals too have their 'moods', in which we may include such states as hunger and repletion, sleepiness, contentment or restlessness, solitary and gregarious, mating and parental moods, and many others.

Before we go further into such basic moods, here is an example illustrating the effects of a change of mood: it is taken from R. A. Hinde's observations on the great tit (1953) referred to in a previous chapter. In the early spring, when the tits are still in small bands, the first mating mood comes over them and makes them aggressive towards each other; as a result of this they begin dividing up into different territories, which later they all do without exception. The mating mood is at its peak in the morning and towards evening, and the birds are least affected by it during the afternoon. At this low point in its power, another slumbering mood comes to the surface and dominates them for quite a short time: the tendency to come together in flocks, which is also prevalent at the seasons of sexual respite. These relapses into a relatively 'sex-free' social mood do not stop until the weeks of spring with the increase of forces making for preservation of the species. Incidentally, without intensive research into the tits' 'every-day' life, such intimate changes in the rhythm of that life could never have been deduced.

*   *   *

To understand how biology works from the external to the internal, we must look briefly at recent changes in the concept of the organism. Experiments have proved the reality of a system or systems directing inner conditions, though they have so far not been exactly localised, and the terms used for them—such as 'centres', 'organisers', 'evocators'—are under constant scrutiny, just as biological ideas of these systems are recognised as incomplete and temporary.

The process of development carried out by a fertilised animal egg-cell lays the foundation of all structures with which the individual to be born must begin meeting his inanimate environment and also members of his species, enemies, prey, and forms of life indifferent to him. A sea-urchin must do so only a few hours after the egg has been fertilised, whereas with a spermwhale it takes about 16 months and with an elephant 22. This reminds us of the great differences in differentiation level, but it is a peculiarity of Man that despite his higher level of differentiation he has to meet his environment far earlier than the elephant does. Such differences are also to be found in the social insects: bees' embryonal period is over after three days, while with termites it lasts at least three weeks—fifty to sixty days on average with termites in cold climates. No wonder the new-born bee is a helpless maggot, while the new-born termite is a very active and mobile larva. The level of differentiation of an adult animal is not dependent on the time it takes the embryo to mature.

The central nervous system as directing apparatus is organised by this process or development, though the passive 'is organised' begs the question of who or what does the organising. To take a simple experiment, if you cut a free-living flat worm (*Turbellaria*) into two halves, each half will re-form into a complete worm: a remarkable feat when you come to think of it, perhaps especially for the rear half! From a mass of embryonal cells this bit of worm creates a completely new nervous system to 'direct its activities'. Its protoplasmal structure must be controlled by some 'organising system' to make such regeneration possible. It may happen several times with a worm, whereas with higher animals' structures it can only happen once, in the embryo's early development. Nevertheless, there is a similar controlling system in the embryonal development of all higher forms.

We know from experiments that many combinations of movements—e.g. wriggling and crawling—are formed already in the development of the embryo and come to completion even though no movement at all is possible during this time. Every embryo has a great many of such innate automatisms and rhythms of movement, just as we know from countless experiments that many connections of sense and effector organs are brought into action by relatively simple innate mechanisms and are there 'waiting', ready to function, long before they are in fact used. There may be more of them in some forms of animal life than in others—say in birds than in mammals; but the contrast within these groups is considerable.

Even though this is a simplification, and we do not know what actually happens in the process, let us for the time being take the simile of connecting pieces fitted in important centres of these structures. Outside influences, i.e. learning and experience, contribute in varying degree towards the shaping of these pieces. In the highest animal forms such centres remain 'open' throughout life, i.e. they are so constructed that they correspond, however vaguely, to the organisation on which our own orientation and learning are based. In other words, as we saw in discussing instinct, animal behaviour may be much more plastic than is often thought, even in instances where it is largely fixed and instinctive.

But there is another side we have so far neglected in our blueprint of how cells develop; and that is the growth of hormone-producing glands, so much discussed today, which secrete substances into the blood or other ducts of the animal body. The most various organs are constructed so that they will afterwards respond to the working of these glands. A full hierarchy of them has been discovered for vertebrates, and also for insects and crabs—we came across them, of course, in connection with the fiddler-crabs' colour-change; and much the same applies to cuttlefish, which are in many ways comparable to insects and vertebrates. In higher organisms these ductless glands act both with and against the nervous system, like a special organ for controlling various processes. We must not say that the hormones 'cause' changes of mood or inner condition, because the cause is really the interplay of separate factors: the special sensitivity, in the colour cells of the fiddler-crab's skin, for instance; the connection of the hormone-producing glands with the central nervous system; the relations of the sensory organs to the brain; and also the unknown structures of the brain which react to the stimulations of the senses. All these preconditions for a change of mood raise the problem of the order which directs such a complex; and so our picture of the organism's structure brings us back to where we started—the analysis of inner conditions.

*   *   *

Let us now turn to a colourful family of exotic fresh-water fish, which zoologists call cichlids; in the last two decades they have received intensive study in many laboratories, which has led to important results. Today we know about 450 species, 300 solely from Africa's interior, and new ones are always being discovered (Plates 24-26).

Hemichromis bimaculatus, one of the African cichlids, is the species we are concerned with for the moment. Apart from the sexually mature forms, these fishes, like some of their relatives, live together in shoals. A brownish red is their predominant colour, though younger ones sometimes have a bit of green on their back and tail. But when mating time approaches, both sexes become a brilliant red (and there are many other changes in the fish's appearance). The behaviour too is quite different. They stop living together in shoals; the males become aggressive and split up; each male occupies a territory at the bottom. If another member of the species enters this, the owner of the territory raises his dorsal fins and moves towards the intruder; his colouring becomes still more striking. In most cases the body looks bigger too, owing to the spreading of the fins. The gill-cover

Plate 19. Sickle-billed paradise bird *(Epimachus)* lives in two species at a height of 5,000 to 9,000 feet in New Guinea. The male's side-feathers form two 'wings', which rise high in courting ritual and at the ceremony's climax close together to a dark shield, on which the pale yellow of the gaping throat is reflected. The external tail-feathers may be moved like claws in quick succession. *After a picture by W. A. Weber in* National Magazine.

Plate 20. Young starlings *(Sturnus vulgaris)* in unfledged dress. We are looking into the box from above: the golden yellow throats gape, and the effect is enhanced by the light yellow of the expanded beak-swelling. The tongue, shaped like an arrow point, is visible in the oral cavity.

Photo: Emil Weitnauer.

carries a black eye-spot, shaped like an oval—which shows
how very much the colouring of 'optical' structures is reckoned
by its effect on eyes. For the oval is so directed that it becomes
visible in the front of the fish when the gill-covers are spread very

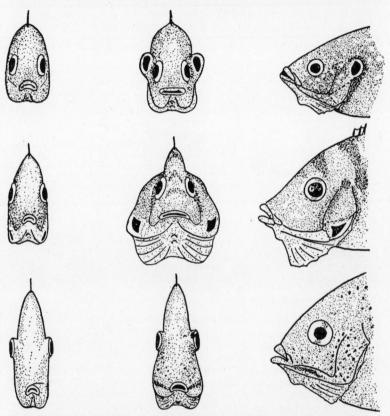

FIG. 18. Transformation of frontal aspect in cichlids through spreading of
gill-cover and its membranes. Above, jewel fish (*Hemichromis bimaculatus*);
centre, *Cichlasoma meeki*; below, *Cichlasoma severum* (after Baerends and
Baerends-van Roon).

wide, and then appears foreshortened as an eye. So the fish
shows an extra 'pair of eyes' to the intruder: the frontal aspect
looks like a very impressive mask. He swims round the intruder
to impress him optically, and tail-beating begins—through the
sense organs down their sides, fish are very sensitive to such

movements of water. Again and again with mouth wide open he charges and circles round the intruder in repeated 'offensives'. Sometimes both fish suddenly get hold of each other with their mouths, pulling and pushing each other and nearing the bottom in the process (Figures 18 and 19).

Usually the intruder soon gives up and quickly retreats upwards. Such fights do not end in death and seldom even with

FIG. 19. Attitudes of *Tilapia natalensis*. Above: rest phase; left, male in depression of the nest; right, female (lighter colour). Centre, left: the rivals seen from the sides (spreading fins, blowing out of throat region); right, male alarmed (compare position of fins with rest phase). Below: intra-territorial fight between two males; left, circular swimming with throat region very much expanded; centre: pushing by one male; right, end of this 'scene'—intimidated, one of the fighters adopts submissive position, which is like the female's pattern. We notice the black in the jaws of the adult male, the colour contrast being enhanced by the white lips (after Baerends and Baerends-van Roon).

serious damage to either side. The retreating fish generally adopts an attitude conspicuously different from that of the territory owner: dorsal and anal fins are pressed tightly against the body, the tail-fin is folded together; it is very like the attitude with which the female acknowledges her submission. This change of attitude, which at once 'declares' the intruder's 'change of mind', is answered almost immediately by the territory-owner stopping his offensive: in other words, his aggression is inhibited by the other fish's attitude of inferiority, which in a sense he may be said to 'understand' or 'perceive'. So the fight ends (Figure 19). Such attitudes of submission or inferiority are to be found in all higher social life, and their discovery has been an important step forward in the understanding of animal's group behaviour.

From the general results of research into hormones we can draw up a plan of how the 'change of mood' occurs which decides the transition from living in shoals to occupying a territory. A hormone of the pituitary gland, the so-called 'gonadotropic hormone' (i.e. directed on the germ-glands or gonads), brings a row of these changes into play. Its effect is above all on the testes and ovaries, in which it causes the maturing processes to begin. But it also brings tissues to maturity in the germ-glands which produce hormones not sex cells. So these hormones of the glands—different substances for both sexes—have their powerful effects on two quite different sides of the organism: peripheral in the appearance and central in the 'mood'. In the skin they are stimuli releasing all the changes which cause the mating dress; while in the brain they work on structures (as yet unknown) which have a high rank in the hierarchy of nerves and thus play an essential part in forming the inner condition.

The influence of such substances can thus affect 'mood' and the consequent selection of activities. The pattern of connecting centres now stimulated and those excluded for the time being decides not only what the animal shall now do but which parts of his environment he will register in this mood and at this moment, and which parts will sink for him into complete non-existence.

These hormones, then, are a sort of mood-instigator. The central nervous system is ready to react beforehand, but it is only the appearance of the sex substances, brought by the blood-stream from the germ-glands, which evokes the new condition, which in turn alters the behaviour. The faculties which kept the fish together in shoals become blocked, while others are activated which make them separate into territories and fight.

No one can yet analyse the systems which are influenced by hormones, or say how they function. But the concrete phenomena we observe as behaviour and the inner structures of brain and hormone-gland, co-operating as experiment has revealed, are alike evidence for a change of inner condition or 'mood': part of the animal's inner life which can be objectively acknowledged with complete certainty.

*   *   *

When the cichlids are already in their full brilliance and the males are spiritedly defending their territories, a sudden shock may in a moment change their inner condition and with it their behaviour. Switch a bright light on to them or splash the water in their bowl with your hand, and they will at once lose colour (with *Hemichromis* the red fades more slowly than the gleam of scarlet), stop defending their territories, throng into a corner in terror with their fellows, and for a while come to live in shoals again as before mating. It is not certain whether this dramatic response to a shock may occur through the effect of hormones. Baerends and Baerends-van Roon (1950), whose account I have here followed, think this is not the case, but it remains an open question. At any rate the phenomenon shows us how quickly the inner state may change, and reminds us the more strongly of what biological research cannot reveal: experience.

It is not only in vertebrates that we know of these 'mood-glands'. Studies of insects have already discovered a good many of them, which provide the preconditions for moultings and metamorphoses and doubtless also for the reproduction functions. Of course insects' internal organisation is different from vertebrates'; and because testes and ovaries produced no actual sex hormones in insects, research into insect hormones was more or less stopped in the period, a few decades back, when these hormones were the new rage. Its resumption is quite a recent development in research into invertebrates, and we shall soon be learning much that is new about the change of inner states such hormones can produce in cuttlefish, crabs and insects.

Biologists used sometimes to call states like hunger, thirst, the sexual and nursing urges, 'physiological states'. But it seems better today to keep the relatively open expression 'inner states' from the sphere of experience, in which we know most about ourselves and which is directly connected with appearances. Howard, the pioneer of behaviour research, says with point: 'if we use the words reflex, conditioned reflex, automatic, instinctive, and do not add the words remembrance, expectation, power to refer—interpretation is vain.' (1940.)

Of course we have no direct access to animal experience, and even with the highest animal forms our indirect access is very meagre. But it is now realised that we shall have a much more accurate idea of living creatures if, parallel with increasing differentiation of animal groups, we credit them with an increase in their inner states, which must be revealed with all the evidence we can obtain of this closed realm. Admittedly we are here on the boundaries of biology, where many biological concepts are inapplicable.

D. Lack, for instance, one of the leading British behaviour research-workers and ecologists, says (1941): 'The concept of an internal drive, which is both a distinct entity forcing the bodily machine into action and, at the same time, part of that machine and created by it, while useful within limits as an analogy, involves insurmountable conceptual difficulties when pressed too far.'

This brings us back to our account of the organism's origins, which I have brought in because, among other reasons, it involves us in the same difficulty. The central nervous system is 'both a distinct entity' which controls the organism, 'and at the same time part of that organism and created by it.' The ambiguity referred to by Lack is a fundamental feature of all organisms: they 'differentiate *themselves*'! However mysterious this may be, no developmental physiologist would doubt the facts which eminent research scientists worked on so intensively between 1918 and 1935.

*   *   *

Lack's remark also leads to the problem of scientific language in general. Although Man did not *make* himself, scientists feel

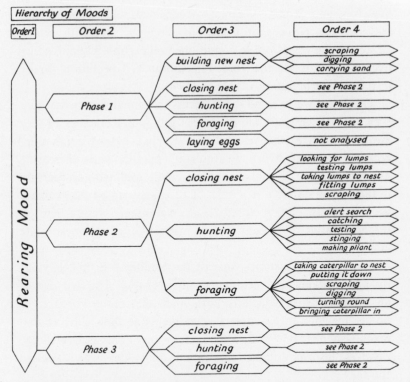

FIG. 20. Mood diagram for a female *Ammophila*. Activities shown here are clearly separated patterns of action, which the observer can establish with certainty. This hierarchy of moods is the result of behaviour research; how the orders are created in the nervous system is not at present known (after Baerends, 1941).

at home with things Man has made, and will naturally use language stemming from such things. Once they leave this bright, clear world of conscious 'making', they still need words to supply the images and analogies for the processes of an unfamiliar, non-human world. A word with mechanical origins is relatively useful so long as I am describing functions or organs which obviously work in a mechanical way. I can call the heart a motor or a pump, if I disregard many of its characteristics, especially the way it develops; and with the same qualification can make a great many points about our motor system with the technical terms applicable to a lever device. But when we venture into the border regions of developmental physiology and research into innate factors and the motives of behaviour, many terms from every-day speech and the world of machines will alike be inadequate, yet we must still find new images to reflect the qualities of a newly revealed world.

Behaviour research has made an important advance by penetrating into the reality of such hidden factual states as animal moods, and by trying to discover their hierarchies—without assuming that there are morphologically provable centres corresponding to them. It is hard enough to establish such an order with human moods, fluctuating, transitory and complex as they are. Yet there we have the inestimable advantage of communication, whereas with animals the research worker is almost always completely excluded from their actual experience. No one will deny the value of an investigation which tries to unite experimentally in particular fields the findings of neurology and those of behaviour analysis. But on the whole the most fruitful way forward may be to improve behaviour analysis so far that the suggested hierarchies can claim to be a piece of observed reality (Figure 20).

Certainly it is important to remain constantly aware that the animal organism is a highly mysterious business. As Tinbergen said in 1953, the behaviour research worker must be prepared for a long period to devote himself to pure observation, so as to become really familiar with all the moods which determine animal behaviour; and he emphasised the failure of experiments where too little attention was paid to changes of mood.

7

The Realm of Images

THE DRAGONFLIES' SUMMER wedding, the grasshoppers' concert, the butterflies' meeting, the ceremonies of the fiddler-crabs and cichlids—all that has made us familiar with effects which originate from members of a species, are apprehended by a partner and receive an appropriate response. The astonishing way in which a fish defending its territory gives up its aggressiveness as soon as an intruder adopts the submissive attitude, shows us the precision of such a response, and is comparable to the immediacy with which the threat of a bite is lifted when one of two fighting dogs makes a gesture of submission. The formation of the central nervous system in dogs and fishes is extremely different, of course, but it is one of the most important results of present-day behaviour research that we can see correspondences of behaviour between animal groups with such dissimilar structures and at such varied levels of differentiation.

From animal experiments with models, we have also learnt that the release of responses may in many cases be produced by very simple forms, which show only a few characteristics of the full stimulating phenomenon. The experiments of Tinbergen and his colleagues have justly received extremely wide attention He replaced rival sticklebacks by all sorts of fish models which were much more globular or flatter than the 'original', yet they all evoked aggressive movements towards them on the part of the male stickleback, as long as their underside was a brilliant red. On the other hand, even a model which resembled the stickleback body very closely produced no aggression in the absence of this apparently decisive red. A male stickleback, in fact, may be stimulated to attack by an object with very few special marks, provided the object is within a certain size limit and shows the mark 'red underneath' (Figure 21).

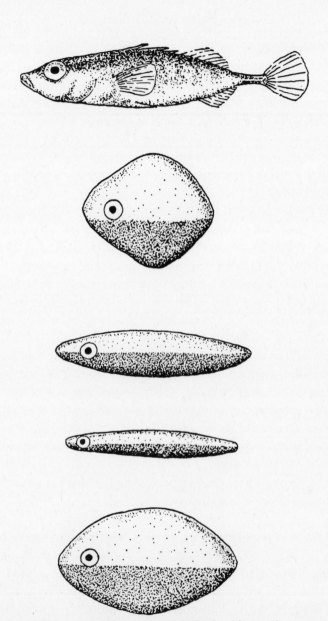

FIG. 21. Models representing male stickleback. Above, the exact copy, but without red, is ineffective. The four deformed models below have the important characteristic 'red underneath' and are therefore effective (after Ter Pelkwijk and Tinbergen, 1937).

However simple the releaser, it must always have a 'form'; the essential parts must be in particular relative positions; and the way the model is held on presentation can have a decisive influence. Similarly young ruminants, so far as they are suckled standing, will seek a mother's nipple in the angle between vertical and horizontal: according to Hediger (1952), this is part of their innate behaviour patterns. At first they also do so on the wrong leg, till this innate geometrical element becomes more complex by learning processes.

We are far removed from the very elementary 'effects' which occur at the simplest social stages, where a chemical substance, a shadow, a spectral colour may often be a releasing factor. These more complex structures we are now considering need more than a sum of stimuli jumbled together; the stimuli have to be arranged in a particular way. We have not only left the sphere of the quantitative for that of the qualitative, but within the latter have gone from the undifferentiated single stimulus to the far richer, higher world of stimulus situations or *Gestalten* (organisations of stimuli)—the German word is untranslatable, and has been retained in English, e.g. in Gestalt-psychology. All life in societies, every actual social urge, functions on this level. It is the level which permits of sociability or gregariousness, among the most astonishing of natural phenomena and with the most far-reaching consequences. For these *Gestalten* direct the energy processes of the whole animal, producing the changes which we can directly observe in its behaviour.

*   *   *

There is a well-known experiment with models which has young chickens and ducklings as its subject. A mechanical flying bird is moved above their heads, which is like a hawk in flight when it is moved in one direction, like a duck or goose in flight when moved in the other. A new *Gestalt* is thus formed according to the direction of the movement, and it in fact has effects which are correspondingly different: when it appears as falcon, the young birds respond by crouching and keeping still—

older cockerels sometimes with aggression; when it appears as goose, it produces no reaction. To appreciate the full mystery of the animal's inner life, it cannot be sufficiently stressed that the impression of a 'hereditary enemy'—nowhere could this phrase be used more accurately—is already prepared through innately fixed structures (Figure 22).

J. von Uexküll has pointed out a corresponding fact at a simpler stage of organisation. Several larger species of scallop (*Pecten*) have along the edge of their shells a row of simple eyes: 40 to 60 with most species, up to 100 with larger species. These eyes, says von Uexküll, 'serve simply to direct the only free movement the scallop is capable of, swimming. What happens is most

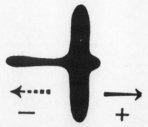

FIG. 22. This bird-model means different things for young nidifugous birds according to the direction of its movement: in the direction marked − it is taken as a duck and is harmless; in that marked + it is taken as a bird of prey and is dangerous (after Krätzig, 1940).

interesting: a darkening of the horizon works on the many small tentacles surrounding the eye and makes them move apart, so that the eye has a clear field of vision. The image of an approaching object is thereupon projected on the retina. Its shape and colour have no influence on the scallop: i.e. the image on the retina is not used as stimulus. But a releasing stimulus is produced by a movement at a very particular speed, the exact speed of the deadly enemy of all scallops, the starfish *Asterias*. Then the blocking action of the big tentacles round the eye is relaxed, thereby allowing the water to come in and be expelled again, so that the tentacles float like long streamers against the moving object. If it is a starfish, their receptors are affected by mucus, so that the tentacles go back. But at the same time a violent wave of stimulation rushes to the visceral ganglion, which responds by stimulating the movement muscle, the swift jerks of which lift the scallop upwards and by strong swimming take it out of the dangerous vicinity of the enemy.'

The images by which a young animal is tied to its nursing parents may be particularly simple and dramatic. Several biologists have investigated these in mouth-breeding fish, and I have selected the *Tilapia* fish as an illustration. As with many

FIG. 23. *Tilapia* young swimming back to their mother. About 10 to 12 days after leaving the egg they are for the first time allowed to swim on their own; before that they 'nest' in their mother's mouth. About 4 or 5 days after their first independent swimming they are not taken into the mouth again. Here they are swimming to dark places: gill-openings and eyes appear like the mouth (after Baerends and Baerends-van Roon).

other species, the *Tilapia* female keeps her spawn in the wide hollow of her mouth till about the ninth day after spawning, and from then on sends out the shoal of small fry to swim under her supervision. In case of danger they all throng round her head, and she snaps them into her mouth (Figure 23).

Baerends and Baerends-van Roon (1950) replaced the female fish with wax models of the most varied sort. All conceivable structures, including some quite unlike fishes, of very different sizes and colours, achieved the same result: when the model was violently moved, the shoal of small fry first scattered to the bottom; when quiet returned, they all swam up to their model now resting peacefully above them. If it had openings, they swam into these. So they have a first, extreme reaction to violent movement of water (flight to the bottom), and a second, subsequent reaction: congregating by the mother and swimming into her mouth. They are also decoyed by dark spots (as 'hollows') and therefore swim towards the dark pupils of their mother's eyes as a possible shelter. The whole response is to a high degree innate, as is shown by experiments with young fish completely isolated from soon after birth, which react to models in exactly the same way. The *Gestalt* of the mother is very vague and open. In Peters' experiments with another species, *Haplochromis multicolor*, it seems rather more fixed: the small fry swam up more confidently to all models compressed at the side than to other models; the presence of eyes in the model also seemed to encourage swimming up to it (Figure 24).

To find out how these mysterious *Gestalten* work, we must start from the facts which have already been discovered from observation. The first of these, in the case of the small fry, for instance, is that they respond to a combination of stimuli which they can never have met before in this form, but which represents something conforming to their species. They must therefore have in their nervous system a disposition which makes such a response possible—which must be already there 'waiting', in fact, before the combination can work on the nervous system.

We are accustomed to 'perceiving' things and occurrences in our environment—an external world crammed full of shapes, sounds, scents, etc. It is inaccurate to say we are used to receiving images of things. For it is first of all a very complex knowledge and experience which brings us eventually to such perceptive *judgment*. Originally, confining it to the activity of our eyes, we simply see things, occurrences, colours, in places outside ourselves; and behaviour research suggests that animal experience has a similar basic form. This perception is so habitual and taken for granted that we scarcely think what an amazing process it is; but if we try to analyse it, we see how very little there is about it of which we can be really sure.

Let us keep to optical perception, as model for other types of it. We know that what we see is not simply what is registered by the retina, however primary and essential these processes are.

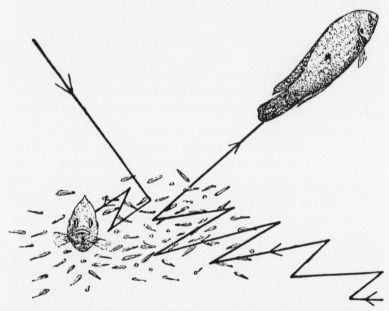

FIG. 24. Relieving of mate by *Cichlasoma biocellatum* parent. If the young are intended to follow, the old fish swims in sharp zig-zags. The relief in nest-digging therefore occurs, in contrast, by rapid swimming in straight lines, so that the young shall not be misled. With this species the parents at once pick up the fry as they emerge from eggs fixed to the bottom, and carry them in the mouth to the prepared nest hole, which is guarded. The change of nests has been correlated with care for nest hygiene (after Baerends and Baerends-van Roon).

It is not as if we were sitting before a television screen in the brain. When I turn my eye from right to left, a continual alternation of stimuli appears on the retina of my eyes, but I see a stable environment; my central nervous system carries out the task of co-ordinating the impressions of many sensory spheres, enabling me to see these impressions not 'in me', but all 'outside', in the world. From this mysterious process of experiencing environment at all, it is only a small part which concerns us now.

The effects of a visual kind, which work on our 'small fry' from the 'mother-figure', are transformed in the retina of their eyes into nervous stimulations—a conversion of energy of special interest to the physiologist. So many nerve fibres extend from the eye to the brain, so many stimulations, different in kind and degree, arrive at the brain for further 'processing'. If they were merely registered in unknown centres, copied and adapted again to the image of the external world, the young fish could do nothing with this copy. He would have to 'learn' them eventually through many repetitions and combinations, learn how to behave towards them, whether attraction or aversion is the 'correct' response; he has to do this with plenty of things in his life. This would be a first learning process through which habits could gradually form—a process almost impossible to grasp when it happens to ourselves, which it is doing all the time.

But the experiment with the isolated young fish shows that he needed no such learning process as regards this particular stimulus situation. What is different then in the fish organism? We can only answer in a very general way. Its whole nervous structure must have an innate faculty for evolving the image of its mother or protector, a disposition the over-all stimulation of which can release complex effects—the behaviour towards its mother which we have seen. Experiment has already shown that the disposition has a few very variable elements in a fixed order.

Our generation has come to accept in various art-forms that considerably distorted images are representations of reality. We might take a lead from these art-forms for the moment, and not regard with too much naturalism the images which finally 'mean' a mother-figure for the young fish. The study of animal behaviour shows us very often that higher animals' experience is not at all 'naturalistic' in the sense that would satisfy naive art-lovers. The models which in many experiments release a particular

behaviour might sometimes very well have been created by con-
temporary artists!

*   *   *

The nervous processes which enable us to find our way in the
world of experience, to deal with things and people, are hidden by
the very nature of our structure: consciousness could not concentrate on experience, that is, unless there was an 'unconscious'
carrying out its work largely unnoticed. Biologists among others
have to probe these hidden processes, though often obliged to use
language from the world of experience. In the present case,
therefore—the young fish of the mouth-brooding group—the
best term to use would seem to be 'image', suggesting a mental
picture or copy: the young fish have an image of the protecting
mother innate in their central nervous structure and prior to all
experience.

What happens is something like this. Co-ordinated groups
of impulses, differentiated in quality and quantity, reach the
central parts of the nervous system, where they are passed on,
modified, connected with each other, but still arranged in such a
way that they keep something of their original character. They
are then brought to the innermost nervous structure, which is so
disposed that particular parts of them fit into parts of the structure, bringing them alone into a new state of stimulation. Built
into the embryo through innate development processes, this
innermost structure with its specially adapted parts is 'waiting'
for special combinations of stimuli—like a telephone switchboard
with connections waiting to be plugged in and 'put through'.
This analogy from every-day life is useful, because having invented
the telephone we more or less understand its workings; cyber-
netics and electronic brains say little to us at the moment, but a
coming generation brought up on them will probably use analogies
from these spheres to bring to light new facets of scientific truth.

The responses going out from the structural field thus stimulated are not exploratory but firmly fixed by ways of reaction that
have become innate—with our young fish, for instance, by

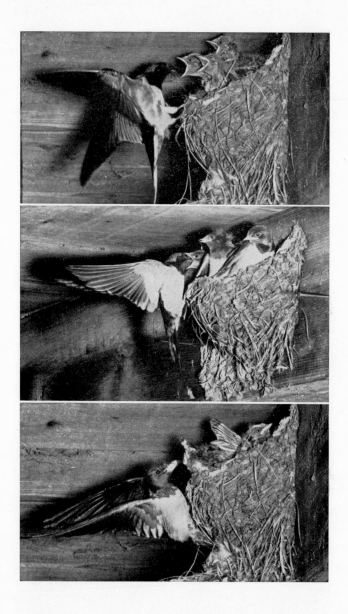

Plate 21. In the nest of the chimney-swallow *(Hirundo rustica)*. Above: the exactly aimed flight directed on a gaping beak. Centre: the old bird's head for a moment thrusts deep into the chick's beak. Below: immediately afterwards the chick turns to release droppings, and the old bird flies away with the gleaming white balls in their clean covering.   *Photo: Emil Weitnauer.*

Plate 22. Above: black redstart *(Phoenicurus ochruros)* feeding. At this advanced age the chicks gape directly at the old bird. *Photo: Emil Weitnauer.*

Below: reed-warbler *(Acrocephalus scirpaeus)* feeding a young cuckoo. The little bird's head almost disappears in the gaping beak of its huge foster-child. *Photo: Hans Traber.*

Plate 23. Not a singing starling but a starling chick 21 days out of the egg. As soon as feeding brush appears, this already fledged bird relapses into childish behaviour, and gapes, spell-bound, incapable of moving even to the brush. In the role of an old bird we must push the brush to it, thus helping the innate co-ordination. *Photo:* Zoological Institute, *Basle*.

Plate 24. Above: jewel fish *(Hemichromis bimaculatus)*, a cichlid from the warm fresh-water of north and central Africa. When at large up to 6 inches long. A species very intensively studied in recent years. Below: *Cichlasoma meeki,* distinguished by the red of throat and belly, comes from the fresh-water of Central America, grows up to 3 inches long and is one of the most beautiful of the New World cichlids.   *After Holly, Meincken and Rachow.*

swimming up to the 'mother figure' found outside, seeking out dark places which the fish does not 'know' might be openings but which he is bound to make for. He spots here what he has never seen before, but what is necessary for the preservation of the species.

We have already met such 'discoveries' with the dragonfly males and females. For two or three years, remember, they have lived as larvae at the bottom of ponds, over which they later fly. They have never had any chance to 'learn about' the strange sexual equipment they will afterwards have, nor to 'learn' the image of members of their species, let alone of a sexual partner. They find both species and partner through innate dispositions.

                    *   *   *

The behaviour of insects and other groups with relatively simple nervous structures (compared to those of vertebrates) is almost entirely based on such innate forms of knowledge. We find this most strange and mysterious, knowing about different forms of knowledge, acquired through probing and making mistakes, learning and relearning, continually revising our image of what the world is like. It is no wonder that most of the best known studies of insects in the past, from Réaumur and Rösel von Rosenhof till the time of J. H. Fabre, have treated them as the opposite pole to our own environmental experience. The strength of this idea has exerted great pressure on modern biologists, who have only freed themselves from its grip with great difficulty.

The more an animal resembles our own general organisation, the more we expect it to share the type of experience we are familiar with in ourselves. Since the fish's fin and the bird's wing correspond to our arm, since our spinal cord is like that of the other vertebrates, since our eyes and ears have so many points in common with theirs, surely our hidden types of experience must have equally many points in common? This reasonable pre-scientific assumption is profoundly shattered by the careful experimental analyses of birds' and fishes' behaviour (and types of experience to be deduced therefrom) which have only become possible through the work of the last 25 years. Admittedly we find a great deal more of what was expected in mammals, although here too there are a good many surprises.

At any rate we have assumed a central structure to produce innate types of experience, and such a structure must have a dynamic order. Its readiness to emit stimuli, and thereby release the responses adapted to it, may change in accordance with the inner state of the whole animal, its 'mood'. Many structures only reach this degree of readiness when the animal is in the grip of the reproduction drive. In the period when the germ-glands are at rest, such structures are immobilised, disconnected; the combination of stimuli which normally brings them into play, either dies away or meets locking mechanisms—we do not know exactly what happens. But even when they are fully active, an excessive supply of stimuli can exhaust and disconnect the central structure; while on the other hand, if the releasing configuration of stimuli is lacking for a long time, the structure may reach a very high state of readiness, so that in many cases the responses may even be released autonomously. This obliges us to assume a sort of 'peak load' creating a condition in which other central processes instead of the normal external stimulus can trigger off the release.

The care needed in reaching conclusions on such points is well illustrated by D. Lack's observations and experiments in England with robins (1946). In the ownership of a territory the male robin attacks all rivals which come into his territory. The experiments with dummies show very strikingly that a stuffed model with the red breast is attacked much oftener than a grey-brown model without this breast colour. Moreover, an isolated bundle of the shining orange-red feathers from the breast releases on its own such violent reactions that one may be inclined to see in this mark a very simple 'releaser', which evokes the defence behaviour like the turning of a switch. But extensive continuation and variation of the experiments bring new results: the aggressive defender sometimes attacks other birds in the territory, especially flying ones; he also attacks a model when the red breast has been removed, as he does with the isolated bundle of red breast feathers. The dummy, which contains only this bundle is not attacked, however, by all male robins; a special kind and intensity of mood are needed. On the other hand a variant of the experiment shows the high stimulus-value of the breast feathers: if wild male robins are shown a complete stuffed robin, but with the breast painted grey-brown, none of them will attack it—though they all react violently to the bundle of feathers! Lack's interpretation is that clearly distinguishable aggressive actions are released by special *Gestalten*: now a chase, provoked by smaller flying birds; now a direct attack, aimed at a bird which is not flying and has the size of a robin; and finally a deliberately threatening attitude, obviously directed at the red breast, the specific mark of the rival. But Lack also shows that these three types of aggressive behaviour cannot be too sharply separated either in their performance or by their releasing cause, and that there is a considerable latitude as to the form the aggression will take—confined, of course, to the few constellations significant in a robin's life.

There are other peculiarities which Lack discovered in the course of these experiments:—

'It was before breakfast on a cold October morning that the strangest of all results with a stuffed robin was achieved. The stuffed bird had been erected in the territory of a hen robin previously known to be exceptionally fierce, and for the record time of 40 minutes this bird continued to posture, strike and sing at the specimen. She was still continuing to do so when the sound of the distant breakfast gong caused me to interrupt proceedings by removing the specimen from its perch and walking off. By chance I looked back, to see the hen robin return, hover in the air and deliver a series of violent pecks at the empty air. I was able to get to the exact place where I had previously stood, and could see that the bird was attacking the identical spot

formerly occupied by the specimen. Three more attacks were
delivered in rapid succession, but on the last two the bird was
about a foot out in position. She then sang hard but returned
for a final attack, now three feet out of position, while her violent
singing continued for some time longer. . . .

'While the sight of red breast feathers normally excites threat
display from the owning cock robin, there is one particular set of
red breast feathers which does not produce this effect, namely the
red breast feathers belonging to the bird's own mate. Similarly
the hen possesses the shape of a robin but is not struck, and flies
away, but is not pursued. She has even sung occasionally in her
mate's territory without evoking any hostile demonstration.
Clearly the cock distinguishes his hen individually, which is a
warning against interpreting his behaviour too rigidly, since such
individual recognition inhibits the attack normally elicited by any
of the above-mentioned signals.

'Red breast feathers normally cause a robin to give its threat
display (provided the red breast feathers do not belong to the
bird's own mate). But this is true only when the robin is in its
own territory. If it is in strange territory, red breast feathers have
no such effect, indeed they give rise to quite different behaviour,
since they make the robin retreat hastily to its own ground. To
this there is one exception, namely when one robin is trying to
claim territory from another.'

Observations on young mammals also show the extreme
plasticity of the central nervous organisation innately prepared
for behaviour. We know some of the marks of the very first
innate experience material which helps initiate in the new-born
mammal the bond with its mother, essential early discovery of
environment. I am referring only to mammals which leave their
mother soon after birth, which means that they are then highly
developed and have brains considerably matured. In most cases
they are at a high specific level of differentiation; it is important
to point this out because mammals, even more than birds, are so
very far removed from each other at different levels. The brain

of new-born ungulates (hoofed animals) is amazingly large; during its life the brain never reaches more than twice that size, and only one-and-a-half times with horses, zebras, donkeys and llamas—as against seven times the size with rabbits, ten times with hedgehogs, thirty or fifty times with bears. This may give some idea of how much in the way of innate structure the young of such ungulates bring with them on birth.

They are almost always highly developed in nerves and loco-motory organs; in their bodily proportions they are like adult animals, and soon after birth are capable of following them. Such neuro-motor development contributes towards the behaviour which will at once ensure their attachment to the group. We are only concerned, of course, with cases where such behaviour occurs at once, without the possibility of their learning it or coming to it by habit.

From the time of the great American bison-extermination in the second half of the 19th century we know of bison calves which after their mother was shot followed so close to the hunter's horses that they received kicks from its hooves. This urge to follow is supposed to be lost at an age of one to two months. Berger, in his memoirs of hunting in Africa, tells of a buffalo calf (*Syncerus*) which ran after him on the hunt. Heck, whose car drove past a new-born zebra (the mother of which had just taken flight), noticed the young foal running after the car and refusing to leave it. More such observations could be quoted.

They all point to the fact that within the structure controlling the behaviour of this highly developed new-born ungulate, the urge to follow is tied to an innate part which is there immediately at birth and is activated by a relatively variable moving mass. From the few instances we know, it is fixed and 'standardised' in the individual very soon after birth by experience, i.e. by learning processes—when it may also take a human being as mother and so be bound to him or her. Hediger (who compiled the above examples) considered such substitutions the expression of what he often called an assimilation tendency. It offers us a glimpse into part of the innate structures which when activated by *Gestalten* release narrowly limited types of behaviour.

*   *   *

As we have seen, many striking characteristics, shapes as well as colours and attitudes, have been found to be signals releasing particular ways of behaviour. For some time the *Gestalt* of an animal was regarded too exclusively as a collection of such 'releasers' with a poster-like appeal. Biologists today are more reserved, especially as experiments have shown that there can be 'supra-normal' releasers. We will illustrate this with young gulls.

We know that on the first day of their lives, i.e. without any learning process, they demand food by begging movements: that the mother's beak releases pecking and that the red spot on the beak's lower side has a very strong part in producing this effect. Tinbergen and his colleagues presented all possible models of the mother's beak to continually new selections of young gulls. From stuffed models of gulls' heads to simple cardboard models, from various painted and spotted models of heads to mere sticks with spot-marks or flat discs with various beak marks, a host of potential releasers were tested; and also the effects of the angle of presentation, the height above the ground, in fact everything which could be varied. The experimenters thus discovered a model which had a more drastic effect than the normal releaser of the mother's head: a thin stick, painted red, with three conspicuous white stripes at its point. Presented at a leaning position near the ground, this released more reactions than the model of the mother's head!

Similar supra-normal releasers have been found effective with a wide variety of animals (Tinbergen collected them in 1950). Thus Köhler and Zagurus (1937) showed that sand-plovers, whose eggs are pale brown speckled with darker brown, prefer white eggs with black spots. Oyster-catchers preferred a lay of five eggs to the stimulus situation of their normal three. When Tinbergen presented them with similar-coloured eggs of different sizes, they chose the biggest egg, which they could handle least easily, with a diameter more than three times as big as their own eggs. Experiments with grayling butterflies have shown that males ready for reproduction respond most strongly not to models of females with the colouring typical of the species, i.e. a dark grey-brown, but to completely black ones. Models of more than the normal size are also more effective than normal-sized ones.

In such cases, therefore, there are 'slumbering' possibilities of effect which are perhaps never realised. Who knows whether this slumber does not hide potential transformations of species? Conceivably such innate mutations could cause changes working in the direction of supra-normal *Gestalten*: that such black butterflies might in fact come into being, and then, like the Prince with the Sleeping Beauty, awaken slumbering impulses to life. Such processes might lead to the evolution and stabilisation of new races.

B. Petersen and his colleagues in Uppsala showed (1952) that the mountain-white butterfly (*Pieris bryoniae*), related to the ordinary cabbage-white, responded visually with much more vigour to the males of their own species and to the females of the closely related rapeseed-whites than to the females of their own species. These Swedish research-workers put this too in the class of supra-normal release and discussed the possible evolutionary consequences. 'The sexes would doubtless find each other more easily if the *Bryoniae* female were white-winged.' The evolutionary problem has many sides which cannot be dealt with here; at the moment I am merely concerned with evidence that releasers do not always correspond, as would at first sight seem logical, to the characteristics of the natural, normal environment.

We meet the supra-normal in other cases too, which warn us not to consider the normal shapes and colours of effective *Gestalten* as being all that indispensable. Dewar, for instance, (1908) gives cases where a white peacock was preferred by ordinary peahens because he was distinguished by specially 'eroticised' behaviour, by continual courting display. The whole complex disclosure of colour patterns in the normal peacock tail-spread goes in any case beyond the framework of the strictly necessary; and in the above case the more effective albino peacock was without any of those most rich and colourful patterns.

Murphy, incidentally, gives a case where a female albino Emperor penguin had a greater sexual attaction for the male penguin than had the normal females. We do not yet know what exactly happens there; and we also have examples where penguins have maltreated such albino exceptions because they did not correspond to the appearance of the norm.

The idea of the releaser has indeed been both fruitful and stimulating, but it has also helped to show the limits of its validity and provide a warning against over-simplification of the problem.

*   *   *

The displacement of energy which occurs in nervous stimulation when the *Gestalten* are transformed, is probably very small, and the corresponding processes in the nerve centres will also be few. The internal structures may contain a sort of amplifier organisation we know nothing about. At any rate such transformation, as delivered by the sense organs, releases working processes in animal behaviour (by way of the central receiving and transmitting structure mentioned above) which we can scarcely overrate and which are like chemical catalysis. A small long-tailed titmouse, for instance, when 'in the mood' for nest-building, will be induced by a few external stimuli to collect small suitable objects; one research-worker (no doubt with considerable displacement of energy!) counted 1,558 feathers in one of these wonderfully soft nests. The number of feeding visits paid to a nest by a blue-tit pair increases in 16 days from about 310 to a peak of nearly 650 a day. Even in the very last days the apparatus registering entry into the nest still shows about 550. With the great tit (in England)—which starts earlier in the day, about 3 a.m. —we find 126 visits on the first day, 346 on the seventh, 425 on the tenth and still as much as 426 on the fifteenth.

These visits are stimulated—apart from the reproduction 'mood'—by the image of strongly contrasting throat colour and beak swelling, perhaps also cheeping and movements, in fact all the innately controlled behaviour of the brood which starts when they come out of the egg. The transformation of the stimulus situation sets in motion an internal system of astonishing proportions and physical achievement.

Inspired especially by bird behaviour, scientists have made scattered attempts to imagine the energy processes (still unknown) which are at work in the animal which is 'perceiving such images'. It has often been suggested that the central nervous system of birds in brooding mood produces a constant flow of general energy, which during waking hours will carry out the bird's various functions. Whenever a strong stimulus has been released, for instance in opposing brain systems, the course of the stimulus can be channelled into the most varied working structures. In the active phase of bird life it seems to be the case then that 'something' *must* happen even if the 'something' at the moment has no point at all. Some of the phenomena which Tinbergen called 'displacement reactions' fall into this class: when a bird suddenly brushes its feathers or carries out a purposeless brooding movement; when a stickleback digs in the sand as if building a nest; when any animal gets into such a 'clash of moods' in which it does not know whether to flee or fight.

The over-excitement induced in animals by a plane roaring above can release mating actions, as Lack (1941) saw from a low-flying plane in the Kenya National Park: when this monster in the sky appeared, one male ostrich after another sank into the ground and spread his wings as if worshipping it. In such cases cats suddenly begin washing their fur; birds abruptly start singing or pecking on the ground without picking anything up; a turkey may go to a spring and make drinking movements without swallowing any water.

All these, of course, are reminiscent of human actions, like scratching the head when worried, shrugging the shoulders when embarrassed, nervous drumming on the table, sudden outbursts of joyful singing or humming on receipt of good news—also, no doubt, induced by a momentary surge of emotion which must find an outlet. Schoolboys coming out of the classroom exhibit 'displacement reactions' like those of anthropoid apes at the end of an 'intelligence test' set them by psychologists (Armstrong 1950). Here, too, the actions have no direct purpose, and are just an involuntary form of self-expression.

But these comparisons also lead us to important contrasts between our human actions and animals' displacement reactions. The energy processes may well be extremely similar, for the dispositions making any ways of movement necessary are common to all higher forms of life and not specific to Man. But the ways of expression are very different. In such situations the responses of higher animals are real innate co-ordinations, i.e. ways of behaviour which have their place in a normal functioning but can occur in this form as well without any purpose. Of course human beings too may possibly exhibit innate ways of behaviour, like the head-scratching mentioned above, also the embarrassed smile, and perhaps yawning; but most such forms of self-expression are in the sphere of actions and habits acquired by long practice and even skill.

*   *   *

In a study of the cichlids (1940) Seitz discovered a new factor, which Tinbergen (1948) tested and confirmed in experiments with the grayling butterfly. He proved that the beginning of the ceremonial, a sort of courting flight, was released in the male by a complex *Gestalt* (in normal circumstances the female flying past). The best effects came from a dark model fluttering past in typical butterfly fashion and coming as near the male as possible. But where the model was missing any one of the essential characteristics, the shade of colour, the authentic fluttering motion or the close proximity, the effects were less successful. They became instantly more successful, on the other hand, when any one of the parts of the *Gestalt* were 'improved' in the model.

Thus the less effective white model was effective when it came nearer or when it fluttered instead of gliding, and the gliding not fluttering model became more effective when it appeared dark instead of white—and so on.

Tinbergen adds: 'The above experiments show that the response's intensity always goes down in the same way, no matter which part of the stimulus situation is missing. So a particular amount of stimulating substance is necessary. One is tempted to describe this by analogy with a reservoir of substance into which the effects of several stimuli can be thrown indiscriminately. The content of the reservoir stimulates the neuro-motor centre to response in a purely quantitative way, decided simply by the *level*, not the particular content. Needless to say, this is only an analogy; in reality nervous centres and impulses are at work.' (It should perhaps be said that the reservoir simile is very much disputed today, and biologists prefer to use other analogies for these problems in the organisation of nervous energy.)

It is the chief function of many sense organs to transform stimulus processes into freely available energy. They are instruments from which permanent stimuli can go out, like statocysts and the structures in our inner ear which correspond to them. The fly's second pair of wings, transformed into small balancers, also serves such energy production. It is because such a condition is brought about in the nervous system by these means that the muscles of the body can find the right 'mean tension' which is sometimes called 'tone' and is the basis of normal movements. The social organism may be able to use as much energy as it does just because the *Gestalten* with their very wide range are carrying out transforming effects throughout waking hours: they preserve the energy 'level' of the whole nervous system.

The increase in brain size might also be looked at from the point of view of energy processes. It can be interpreted, as it were qualitatively, by reference to increased functions and more complex perception organs; but also by reference to the increased production of energy which goes with the more intensive life of the warm-blooded animal. This indeed is another of those important 'circular' processes: the increased production of energy is required by the more intensive functioning of the whole, and also makes such functioning possible.

*   *   *

Our examples of transformed stimulus situations or *Gestalten* have so far referred chiefly to modified behaviour, but these inner states are also decisively involved in other processes which might at first seem less accessible. As far back as 1911 Craig proved that development of eggs can be induced in the female pigeon by the mere sight of a courting male. In the male pigeon the sight of a brooding female can release the beginning of secretions of crop-milk which pigeons of both sexes have ready as the first food for their young (Patel, 1937). The presence of the 'right number' of eggs can by means of external stimuli stop any more being developed, whereas with some birds (not all) the sight of an insufficient number may induce more eggs to be developed and laid—so that in such cases the performance of the ovaries can be immensely enhanced by taking away eggs.

Here are processes which we sometimes call physiological in distinction from psychological ones, but which are released or checked, controlled and influenced, from outside, through the medium of *Gestalten*; and through 'images', the complex experience of things in the environment which acquire value and purpose through the animals' innate structure or by learning processes. These configurations function in the most various parts of the organism, and they cannot so easily be divided into psychical and somatic.

The examples I have mentioned do not apply to all birds, nor in this extreme form to mammals. But stimulus situations exert their hidden influence on mammals and on Man, even if acting more slowly, well into spheres which are usually thought of as merely physical: hence the favourite medical catchword of 'psycho-somatic'. Biologists have long taken a 'psycho-somatic' attitude (sometimes without knowing it), recognising that there can be no hard-and-fast distinction between physical and mental conditions, which are in fact continually interacting.

Let us return to David Lack's experiments with robins, and in particular to the strange 'attacks' into empty air. Ornithologists know other similar cases, and we meet the inner world here as effective factor in the most striking way. We could not describe such behaviour adequately and scientifically without knowing 'previous history': the robin's attack on his stuffed rival. This obliges us to talk of 'memory' and of an inner condition in which a previously effective stimulus situation has also an after-effect. Although our knowledge of energy processes is so scanty, it seems probable that similar after-effects are at work in animals' moods when they are 'looking for', 'expecting' something, i.e. such effects mobilise structures within the animal in which the later 'recognition' of stimulus situations is prepared.

*   *   *

In the course of this introduction to *Gestalten* we have more than once come across ways of functioning reminiscent of the hidden 'complexes' which psychologists assume to be at work in human life. The reader with knowledge of Jungian thought may well have been reminded of 'archetypes', and indeed Jung postulated these in close relation to the phenomena of higher animal life which used to be called 'instinctive'. From the biological side, Alverdes in 1937 tried to show the effectiveness of archetypes in animals' instinctive actions. It is worth briefly considering how far the conception of archetypes is useful for biology.

These archetypes are supposed to be located in the 'collective unconscious'. According to this psychological hypothesis, the inherited experience of countless generations is deposited in the human *psyche*, like strata in the earth's crust, and is transformed into a collective unconscious—common to vast numbers of people and perhaps to all mankind—which influences all our actions. The archetype is then seen as the copy of 'a hidden psychic structure which is innately ready and without the help of consciousness releases a behaviour that is a psychic necessity.' Clearly, this conception comes near to the *Gestalten* of behaviour research.

Whether the concept of the archetype has meant a great widening of the horizon or is merely an abstraction which had better be avoided (on which psychologists still disagree), biologists will show a certain reserve in adopting such psychological and anthropological concepts. For one thing research into the inner states of animals is still in its early stages, and for all the rapid strides it has made in recent years it must for some while be primarily concerned with extending factual knowledge; only when its theoretical foundations are clarified, as they will be in course of time, can its relations with anthropology become really fruitful. For another thing biology can bring exact proofs for the innateness of particular ways of behaviour among animals, whereas with men such 'archetypal effects' can only be demonstrated indirectly, since they never occur till a later stage in individual life (i.e. not immediately after birth), so that experiments of the same kind as with animals are practically impossible. Even with such an early human behaviour form as laughter, the existence of 'archetypal releasers' is very difficult to prove, though it seems quite probable (see the studies of Kaila and the works of Spitz and Wolf). Most ideas of innate behaviour forms are based, therefore, on comparative investigations: the finding of the same behaviour forms among the most different peoples must rank as evidence for their being innate.

We saw with the digger-wasp *Ammophila* that her 'perceptive behaviour' when inspecting nests was balanced by 'imperceptive behaviour' after the inspections. Such new insights into differentiation in animal behaviour warn us against oversimplified ideas of the higher animals. But they do not always bring Man nearer to animals, as is sometimes supposed; they merely show that far more of what we know in ourselves is to be found also in animals. The more comprehensively anthropology tries to see its subject, the more manifest becomes Man's separateness and loneliness in the whole of living creatures. That makes our relationship to the higher animals, especially primates, an even profounder biological problem—contrary to the popular belief, that all the light needed has been shed on our dark beginnings.

8

Social Life as an Aid to Preserving the Species

THE OBSERVER OF social life must time and again be shifting his attention between two different aspects. In one of these, society is an organisation where the individual has value merely by being a member of it: it is considerably limited in possibilities of self-expression, but contributes towards achievements only realisable in society and is integrated with other individuals for purposes which can be seen only in judging the whole. In the other aspect, equally essential and indeed complementary, the individual finds complete fulfilment only in and through social life, which allows the greatest possible 'individuality' and vitality for individuals. We will consider the former aspect first: social life as an aid to preserving the species.

Because social life is partly a product of evolution, we must briefly consider the whole question of evolution and the doctrines of it which are held today. In the fields of geology and palaeontology, and also that of modern genetics, specially mutation research, there are an overwhelming number of facts to be understood only by reference to the most general idea of evolution. This is that species originate by development from earlier forms, not by special creation; that there is a real 'family tie' causing common features between creatures so different from each other as ostriches from sparrows, deer from whales and wasps from dragonflies; that there is a definite if still mysterious connection in the way fishes, amphibians, reptiles and finally warm-blooded creatures have developed one after the other in the course of 500 million years. 'Evolution' states that such a connection is established fact, but there are many different theories which try to explain that fact.

Darwin's is not only the most important of these historically, but it has been largely confirmed by modern research into what are now called mutations: innate characteristics in the issue of animals and plants, which differ from those of the parental stock and can be passed on in this new form to the next generation—by the chromosomes, special structures in the cell nucleus. If the animals or plants possessing these characteristics are in any way 'preferred by nature' to the forms of life previously existing, they may multiply in numbers as well as keeping the characteristics. In this way the species is gradually transformed in various directions. To explain the transformation Darwin once postulated such inner variants, without being able to prove their existence conclusively; they have now been traced, with full experimental proof, as mutations. New mutations are continually being discovered, indeed special strains and breeds may be new species developing—for although the majority of mutations seem to be harmful some of them give rise to successful organisms and these mutations determine the evolution of the species.

At any rate, to take the results of mutation research by and large, the innate variants discovered can be the building stock for new variants of a species, and most biologists would probably agree to this very general conclusion. To this extent they are all 'evolutionists', but beyond it there is a great divergence of opinion, which depends among other things on the different philosophic attitudes and preconceptions which they bring to their research. We all have these, and should be ready to recognise as far as possible the part they play in determining our judgments. We shall then be less inclined to declare everybody else's views marred by prejudice while our own are completely objective, 'from bias free of every kind'.

Thus some scientists are quite sure that the changes discovered by mutation research are the material for the evolution of all life, i.e. the whole vast range of living things must have developed out of the simplest germs through ceaselessly repeated mutations over millions of years. Those who believe this are commonly called neo-Darwinists, and today they are in the biological ascendant. For them the general problem of life's origins is solved, although details still have to be clarified.

Many biologists, however, are much more reserved as to the range within which mutations can take place, and believe that the Darwinian rules apply only for the origin of sub-species: that the mutations so far known, sometimes called micro-mutations, carry out their transforming effect within a species; but that where greater variations occur (macro-mutations)—for instance between birds on the one hand and mammals on the other—it is a process of quite a different kind. Some experienced scientists, such as R. Goldschmidt, are convinced that experimentally produced macro-mutations are already established in particular cases, so that the basic processes of evolution are known to us. Others, such as B. E. Guyénot, consider that besides micro- and macro-evolution a special way of evolving must be accepted for the largest units of organic life (mega-mutation). Some biologists see this as the last consequence of an immense succession of micro-mutations, others as a completely unsolved mystery.

Those of us who cannot go the whole way with the extreme, neo-Darwinist theory of mutations, as explaining all the phenomena of evolution, are influenced partly by the vastness and complexity of the facts to be explained, but also by a realisation of how completely theories will change with some new discovery— e.g. the new insights into the composition of the atom. Nobody could have guessed beforehand what that composition would be, or at the occurrence of these erratic changes called mutations. As soon as we leave the field of everyday experience for that of protoplasm, all the empirically discovered structures and processes come as a surprise to the human observer, and are likely to upset his previous theories.

*   *   *

According to the tenets of neo-Darwinism any ways of behaviour which exist show positive value for selection by the very fact of their existence. Whatever exists must once have come into being, and could only have survived through a positive fitness for survival. Why it came into being is left open, or at least for most geneticists it is not due to purposeful directing factors, which only apply to the preservation of what has once evolved. Even an insignificant variant in behaviour may have selection value, may work favourably in enough single cases for it to be preserved through the generations, and also gradually spread, so that in the end it becomes the prevailing characteristic in larger groups of individuals of a species.

Variations in social behaviour are also part of the selection process, as has been brought out more and more by the research into social life of the last twenty years. Of course the elementary functions of society in preserving the species had been known long before: e.g. that swarming and migrations make an essential contribution to preserving the species, especially where (as with many fish species) eggs and sperm are emptied into the water without external mating organs. Similar elementary functions are fulfilled by all drives impelling members of a higher species to find each other and thereby make contact with the opposite sex. Behaviour research has shown more particularly how at higher levels of animal life the conflict between different drives has in various ways contributed towards these animals' preservation, expansion and development. We will try to see this side of things a little more clearly.

My first illustrations will be from the sub-social life of highly developed insects, and we turn once more to the dragonflies. It will be remembered that the females, in other genera besides *Calopteryx*, often stray some way from the water, while the males are more tied to it. Here they wait, flying up to any moving object of a certain size, fiercely defending their small territory of the day. In the last stage of their larval life they come out of the water and shed their nymphal case, equipped only with a few innate behaviour rules: e.g. they must attack flying objects of a certain size; and there is also a vague innate knowledge of the sexual partner. But in the first days they learn a great deal.

For instance, the males on a stretch of bank, after violent clashes in the air, very soon learn to keep in definite zones, within which they hunt prey and patrol; they learn to avoid other males in the vicinity and thus to secure a hunting-ground for themselves. If there is enough demand from males on a stretch of bank, the distribution of these hunting-grounds will sometimes have complete geometrical exactitude.

For the individual dragonfly the separation of hunting-grounds has little or no significance: they would easily find enough prey anywhere in the air, and some might even have better hunting without such territories. But for the life of the species the daily territories ensure the necessary peace and lack of disturbance for mating and the subsequent laying of eggs. Moreover, as a result of the males owning territories, the eggs are laid over a large stretch of bank instead of being concentrated unpractically in a few places. The emerging larvae, small predators of the water, are thus satisfactorily distributed over larger stretches even before birth, so that they do not compete against each other for food in a very narrow space. The seeking of new territories every day also obliges the males to go beyond the familiar stretches of bank in search of new ones, so that they expand the area of the species.

This temporary possession of a sort of territory is not very distinct social behaviour in dragonflies; but while quite without importance for the individual, it clearly has several advantages for the life of the species. Where innate variants occur in particular points of such species-preserving behaviour, these mutations may be 'favoured by Nature' so that they survive and produce subtle variations in the life of the species, e.g. the female going right under water, thereby expanding the area in which the eggs are laid. We saw that with *Calopteryx elegans* something like a new strain or sub-species may perhaps be developing through this characteristic, and the same may apply with some populations of *Ischnura splendens* where the male escorts and stimulates the female in her egg-laying. Particular variants survive because of their preservation value, while other less useful ones lose ground and gradually disappear. There is no 'struggle for existence' in the usual sense of the word 'struggle'; the preservation of the species through selection of the fittest method works far more subtly, and the reasons for the selection can be seen only by careful investigation. We might at first sight have thought it an advantage for the male dragonflies to be able to fly where they liked, but the fact that they are tied to one place proves important for the species: a compulsion on the individual extends the species' freedom.

*   *   *

Our old friends the sand-wasps, with their relatively modest social ties, also shed light on the evolutionary role of social impulses. Here is Baerends again describing an episode in *Ammophila's* daily life:—

'A female occupied with her nest attacks any insect coming near it, from a tiny ant to a big grasshopper. She flies off directly at the enemy, makes periodical charges, and pursues it up to four inches from the nest. Usually this is enough to chase the other insect away; only a few times did I see a wasp gripping enemy insects in her mandibles and tossing them away like a load of sand. These were ants, in one case a velvet ant, which had ventured into or near the nest opening.

'But it sometimes happens that two females whose nests are near together (2 to 6 inches) are both working on the nests at the same time. Then the first to appear attacks the other when she is visiting her own nest. Because all wasps often fly a small distance away from their nests, each of the two plays alternately the part of attacker. So neither of them can work unless the other is absent, e.g. fetching material for closing the nest, sunbathing, etc. Usually in such cases neither wasp succeeds in driving the other off, and a regular wrestling match develops, in which they grip each other in their mandibles and are soon rolling on the ground. I have never been able to observe that injuries occur during the struggle, which generally ends by one of the wasps going off to sun-bathe! The other can continue her work undisturbed until her neighbour returns and the battle starts again.

'They fight over a caterpillar with particular violence. This happens, according to my observations, only when two wasps at the same time lose their caterpillars (e.g. when they have been scared away by men) and when they both think the same caterpillar is their own. I have never seen real "stealing".

'The wasps fight only near their nests or caterpillars; otherwise they get on well together. I have already mentioned this tolerance when they are sun-bathing; they never fight either when passing the night together or while sucking nectar. So there is a territory with the nest in the middle of it. *Ammophila's* territory differs in several respects from the familiar bird territories. Whereas the latter are of different sizes, are usually formed irregularly and often sharply bounded by definite landmarks, *Ammophila's* territories are all more or less circular and of the same size. Birds' territories are also compressable (Huxley 1934), i.e. new birds may come to settle in an area which has already been "shared out"; if such newcomers can hold their own in battle, a new territory will grow up between the old ones and new borders are established. As we have seen above, however, two wasps whose nests are near together never learn to tolerate each other. They fight on till one disappears; the frontiers of the territories do not change.'

Our sand-wasp, governed by her reproduction mood, is under the influence of contrary drives: there is the social bond which makes her seek the vicinity of other members of the species, and there is also an individual tendency at work which drives her to isolation. Because of the contradictory behaviour this produces, the wasps should live in loose communities and establish territories which give a wide enough reserved space round the nest. If the space is too small, as in the cases we have seen with Baerends, the presence of several wasps at the same time repeatedly causes clashes which do not profit the individual and also impede the important business of species preservation. For the time which must be spent in this fruitless strife is lost to the bringing of food or the digging of more nests.

This situation may change through either of two innate variants. The wasps' aggressiveness may be to some extent suppressed, so that nests can be built very close together without provoking time-consuming battles; or else the aggressiveness is increased, which means the clashes are more violent, and nests that are too close are shut down, so that larger territories are formed. Both variants may occur at the same time in the larger wasp populations, quite possibly with the most efficient brood-nurses. The peculiarities of the variant may survive, till they subtly alter in various directions the picture of the sand-wasp's life—through features conducive to preserving the species. Such alterations in behaviour may also be accompanied by fine distinctions in the insects' physical structure. New strains are thus eventually produced which differ in form and behaviour, and this process is doubtless one of the ways in which new species develop. The sand-wasp described by Wilke as *Ammophila adriaansei* (1947) may in course of time have been isolated from the more common species of *Ammophila campestris* and may be dominant in some areas just because it has a working method of simultaneously supplying several nests. Although this does not bring any advantage to the individual, it can give the group ascendancy over the species' original form.

The balance between contrary drives is also achieved in many forms of brood-nursing fishes, especially some other old friends, the cichlids. The self-assertion of the mature males, which occupy and strongly defend their territories, is species-preserving, because it ensures a guarded zone of peace for the spawn's development. If they were less militant, the spawn would suffer, while the possession of a territory is just enough to satisfy the drive to assert themselves: their aggressiveness generally abates towards the borders of the territory, and in a strange territory a submissive attitude is the rule. Through this innately secured order the possession of a territory works as a factor preserving the species, preventing the futile loss of its members and of coming generations. Here again, as with the quarrelling sand-wasps, the subtly working selection processes have created an amazing biological balance between the antagonistic drives towards forming groups and staying separate.

*   *   *

Bird-life at the peak of the mating season is especially rich in such social behaviour, going beyond the elementary needs of the individual's self-preservation and finding its purpose only in the larger whole of the various groups. The actual mating is without result unless the movements are so arranged within a short space of time that the two sexual apertures exactly fit on to each other. Only a few birds, e.g. ducks and ostriches, have a mating organ such as we almost take for granted with the higher vertebrates. The overwhelming majority have very simple apertures for both sexes, and the precision of instincts represents their ancillary equipment. Such instincts are also necessary for the reproduc-tion of mammals, but with birds the couples have to work together much more exactly. This precision, however, pre-supposes full functioning of the internal drives, an optimal mood for mating, which is produced by the extreme effectiveness of the mate's *Gestalt*. The ceremonial handling of nest material, as we can observe with many species, the innately controlled stimulating attitudes, song-birds' singing—all these we have already met as mood-producers, possessing a significance beyond the individual's preservation. They work in the service of the species, the survival of which requires that the right actions take place in different individuals at the right moment.

Let us consider for a moment some peculiarities of hatching. With most reptiles the eggs are left to their fate after the female has laid them in sand or humus or other wet, warm spots. The eggs must therefore be adapted for considerable variations in the surrounding temperature and thus in development time. As they are often unprotected and the young too are almost always

left to their own resources, the mortality rate in young reptiles is
high, and the number of eggs produced in a reproduction period
is always large.

It is very different with birds. The eggs can only develop
within narrow temperature limits, and it is an absolute necessity
that the temperature should remain relatively constant; precision
of hatching time almost to the day is the result. Here we are
touching only the positive possibilities of social life, hatching of
eggs, defending of nest and territory, often too the feeding of the
brooding mate: a chain of tasks which can be performed more
expeditiously and more surely by a pair than if one bird had to
perform them alone. It is not surprising that as bird genera
become more differentiated in brain, their reproduction processes
show greater social complexity, with the number and range of
innately fixed rules increasing progressively. The survival value
of these solutions to social problems is often easy to demonstrate
and always significant. Otherwise such a lot of thriving bird
groups could not preserve and even extend their stock with only
a single egg in the year. If these hatching arrangements were
consciously planned, what an immense amount of intelligence,
will-power, self-control and devotion would have been needed to
ensure they succeeded in their species-preserving purpose. Birds
have a highly organised nervous life, but even with fishes and
arthropods, which have far fewer nerve organs, this factor has its
significance: the smaller an animal's capacity for intelligence and
learning, the more exact and certain must be the structure and
working of its organs of social life.

The evolution of hatching shows that each innate change or
mutation, leading from the reptile state to the optimal brooding
of birds, may achieve value in preserving the species. This of
course has no bearing on the general problem of how reptiles
gradually evolved into birds.

*   *   *

A last example, dealing with the evolution of social behaviour
patterns, will show more clearly how I regard the possibility of

evolutionary change through the micro-mutations which are already known and experimentally accessible.

The species-preserving value of many social structures can in extreme climatic conditions distinguish the life of a species very sharply from its nearest relatives: as is strikingly illustrated by the Emperor penguin (*Aptenodytes forsteri*) of the Antarctic. During the reproduction season, when these penguins live on land, the conditions of existence are more than forbidding. In Terre Adélie, where they were thoroughly investigated by the French Antarctic expedition, they live in temperatures of from −13° to −31° (Farenheit) and endure snowstorms which rage at eighty miles and hour. According to the expedition's doctor and biologist, J. Sapin-Jaloustre (1952), 'a human being is blinded by the ice mask which forms on his face in a minute, whatever his protective clothing; his breathing is laboured, and he finds himself incapable of the slightest effort. A small area of naked human skin freezes in about 40 seconds. If he moves as much as 50 yards from his shelter, he will have lost all his physical faculties including seeing and hearing and any kind of bearing, and will never find his way back.'

In such conditions, in the dark winter of the Antarctic, the Emperor penguins breed. Besides many favourable physical dispositions, they are helped to survive by special modifications in behaviour: e.g. their strikingly motionless waiting in one place, which avoids loss of energy; and perhaps also the production of sounds as means of communication instead of the very 'detailed' gesture-language used by other penguins. The conspicuous absence of many typically penguin ceremonials is bound to work in those border regions of life as a species-preserving economy in the metabolism (Plate 28).

These giant penguins are remarkably peacable, without any aggressive urges, any need for a breeding couple's territory, or any hierarchical order. This is particularly useful at the beginning of a snowstorm, when the colony throng together in a narrow space, forming the so-called 'tortoise-shell', whereby they face the raging blizzard as a compact mass, exposing to it only the smallest possible area of their bodies and completely protecting within the shell the chicks which are specially endangered.

They only become combative where an egg or a chick is concerned, for in Sapin-Jaloustre's description, 'the drive to possess and nurse a chick is common to all the adults, and is so powerful and striking that Wilson called it "pathetic". Immediately a chick emerges from the skin-flap of the parent-bird's stomach, or is left by the parent bird, those penguins which have no chicks vie with each other to take charge of it. Pressing and pushing, the old birds peck dangerously, trying to thrust the chick on to their feet (on which the chicks are isolated from the ice surface of the ground). In the process the chicks are roughly handled, and their skin is often injured. Many are thus destroyed by love! Wilson tells us that they often try to escape and hide in cracks in the ice, to avoid this terrible devotion—that they prefer to starve or freeze to death.'

It thus happens that an egg has many hatchers, a chick many protectors, not only the actual parent birds. By and large, all eggs and chicks are cared for by the whole colony. 'This communal brooding and rearing of young by a succession of old birds means a considerable economy, compared with the family structure of the Adélie penguins (the smaller Antarctic species) at the same stage of reproduction. The old birds can thus afford to spend four or five times as long in the fishing which is so necessary in this climate—all the more necessary just now because they must assuage the chicks' hunger as well as their own.'

As for the evolutionary problem, it is easy enough to appreciate the species-preserving value of any small mutations in behaviour which weaken penguins' normal drive for a brooding territory and limit aggressiveness to the drive to possess an egg or a chick. We can see how a species develops through many such mutations out of conditions such as we find with the King penguin (*Aptenodytes patagonica*) and which finally lead to a way of life adapted to the extreme severity of the Antarctic climate.

The advantage of this habitat—for only such an advantage makes this evolution purposeful—is the extraordinary abundance of food the Antarctic offers and also the complete absence of enemies on land or in the air.

*   *   *

Research into evolution, freshly inspired by mutation studies, has thoroughly established the significance of species-preservation as a factor in social life, and will doubtless find many further examples of such significance. This factor indeed is often used so exclusively in interpreting phenomena that for many biologists a phenomenon is 'explained' if its selection value in a species' social life is shown.

But social life has other aspects which must also be attended to. As a species not only survives and evolves further, but relatively to a particular time simply 'exists' with all its individual members' peculiarities; so the society of animals is not merely an evolving instrument for species preservation, but also an aspect of individual life: individuals 'make' a society, but society is also a factor of life in the service of individuals. It is this side of social life, the other 'pole', to which we must now turn.

9
Social Life and the Individual

THE INDIVIDUAL WORKS towards the preservation and evolution of the social whole of which he is an integrated member. This is the role in which the animal always appears when considered simply as carrier of the continuity of the species. But it is of course a one-sided view, though very tempting with such vast problems to be solved as those of species preservation and sexuality, to which all social biology leads us. The dangers of such one-sideness are illustrated by the zeal with which biologists today will search for 'survival value' in even the finest differentiations of behaviour. I shall scarcely be thought to underrate or disparage this thriving field of study, which rightly has such a strong attraction for young biologists; I hope I have already shown sufficiently my respect for the achievements obtained and for the devoted research which has gone into them. But here I shall try to shift the viewpoint to the individual animal as an 'end' not a 'means'.

Of course we at once come up against the same poles of tension among human beings, and indeed two bitterly conflicting views of the individual's place in society. There is the totalitarian view, for which the individual has value only as a member of society, is 'expendable' and replaceable at any time if society requires it; whereas for the other view the individual, though a natural member of society, has on his own account an irreplaceable value, with rights which society must respect and foster as far as possible (since society's real aim is the production of 'better' individuals). Both views recognise that society's achievements go beyond the sum of achievements which would be possible for individuals on their own; but for the former the great society—the state, the collective, or whatever it may be—

becomes an end in itself, to which mere individuals may be sacrificed without scruple; while for the latter view society's end is to improve the conditions of life and possibilities of self-fulfilment for all the individuals who make it up.

Even biology is sometimes called into the service of the totalitarian view. Exclusive concentration on the individual animal's importance for preserving the species can be used as a biological foundation for any theory of the state as a super-organic entity. But there are many biological facts which show the inadequacy of this approach but still form part of the general picture of society's role among animals. These facts I shall now consider.

*   *   *

There are striking elementary effects in which communal life is seen to be beneficial for the individual animals. It is established that fishes eat more in a shoal than alone, and also grow more intensively, not only because of eating more but from other influences of communal life. Even a comparatively simple organism like the marine flat-worm *Procerodes* stands up better to the variations in salt content (which are so fatal to many creatures of the sea) when in a group exposed to such variations than when it has to face them alone. When a stickleback in a shoal begins to feed, it causes other sticklebacks to imitate it, and thus causes more intensive feeding by the shoal; and this corresponds to what has been observed in flocks of birds. Cockroaches find their bearings better when living in twos or threes than if they are kept on their own.

Such effects are not only material, but are the result of a positive response, however simple, to other members of the species, and they testify to an 'experience', however slight, however small the conscious part of it may be. In the great insect colonies the presence of the royal couple among termites or the queen among bees exerts a strong influence, causing stimuli which fill the insects' lives with changing impressions and variations in behaviour, and thus far greater activity.

This filling of time, with greater variety of relations to the environment, is certainly an important way in which social units benefit the individual animal. As the basic structure is social, the individual animal finds 'fulfilment' through social activities. Just as human beings often go to all extremes to 'kill time' and avoid boredom, so animals can easily become bored—as zoo keepers know, who are concerned to give the animals' time a purpose by training them.

A flock of starlings in the sky on an autumn evening looks like a single organism in the unity of its movement, the precision of its wheeling and climbing and sinking: we feel the single bird has completely given up his individuality to become part of this great flock. There is the same impressive unity in a flock of carrion crows, as day dawns on a winter morning, flying noisily from sleeping places to feeding places and 'the day's work'. Where are these flocks a few weeks later? Vanished, dispersed over a wide area, through the newly awakened seasonal urge to mating, to form the much narrower and quite different society of brooding couples. In early spring we see our carrion crows in the fields always in pairs, not flying round at large, as we might expect, but each occupying a relatively narrow space, the future brooding territory. We can follow such changes through the great tit, which in many respects will serve as representative for a number of other song-birds (R. A. Hinde, 1952).

In winter the tits live in small flocks which roost and fly out foraging together. Among these flocks are the pairs which reared a brood together in the summer, sometimes keeping a little more 'on their own', though without cutting themselves off from flock life. In early spring the males especially often have moments of aggressiveness against each other. The flock slowly disbands, because its members become increasingly affected by new inner states. The males are the first to break loose, and soon they are seen pairing up in a chosen area: the flocking season is once again over. The male now looks for favourite spots in his territory where he can sing. There are a great many of them when the pair first separate from the flock, but soon he shows greater selection, and there are only a few such points, to which he is tied by habit. Finally he develops a clear preference for a particular place, which he defends fiercely. He also defends the area round it, though with less intensity the further he gets from the favourite haunt.

So there develops what biologists call 'ownership behaviour', for it shows a striking resemblance to the human drive towards ownership: M. Meyer-Holzapfel (1952) has made a thorough comparative study of this drive in human beings and in animals. Such a comparison is far more than a piece of 'biologist's licence' to bring nearer home a bird's life. For in the case of these tits, for instance, their inner state, as revealed by external forms and behaviour, can best be described by reference to familiar human experience, however uncertain the relation may be between that experience and the birds'. At any rate the tit pair 'owns'—in a real sense—a brooding territory, which can be expanded in the brooding time or shrink somewhat (as careful investigations have shown).

This territory belongs to the pair: the favourite places make it into a specially attractive environment, in which very soon the nest will occupy a new favourite place. The individual tit is now a creature with its own private space, containing centres of particular importance. This space has its structure, like a magnetic field with lines of force which the physicist makes visible; indeed considering the progressive intensity with which it is defended, we might speak of the tension of the field and the intensity of the various points in it—as long as we manage to keep in mind the special, non-homogeneous character of a living 'magnetic field' (Bally, 1944). Vigorous and thorough investigations have shown this characteristic of territories for a great many species of animals, ever since 1868 when Altum first recognised bird territories, and more particularly since Howard's all-important studies.

Attachment to a place enhances the individuality of the single

Plate 25. *Tilapia zillii*, inhabitant of North African fresh-waters. At large they grow up to 11 inches, in aquaria seldom more than 4 or 5.
Above: two males in unexcited state, fish on right with erect position of fins.
Below: the head of male (right) at reproduction time is velvet black with turqouise spots; throat and chest are blood-red. The female (left) is at this period marked by two white patches on the fins.
After Holly, Meincken and Rachow.

Plate 26. Mating ceremony of *Aequidens portalegrensis,* a big Brazilian cichlid. The colouring difference of the sexes is slight, but the ceremonial is highly developed. Both pictures show the ritual 'mouth-fight' preceding mating.   *Photo: Innes Publishing Co., Philadelphia.*

Plate 27. A big brooding colony of king penguins *(Aptenodytes patagonica).*
The brooding birds are spaced out individually from each other; their brooding places form a regular pattern. A belly fold warms the single egg, which
rests on the feet. *Photo: Niall Rankin,* Life.

Plate 28. A colony of Emperor penguins beginning to form a close group. There is no spacing out as with their relatives *(see* Plate 27).

Photo: Dr. J. Sapin-Jaloustre, French Polar Expeditions.

animal or animals: the male tit singing in his look-out is recognised from a distance by other tits in the vicinity as a particular bird. The territory thus adds distinguishing marks to those of body and behaviour, it becomes a part of the whole individual, also an expression of his capacity for self-assertion. It has its inner side in the bird's experience: he knows his territory exactly, recognises it again when he returns there. Even the cuckoo, laying her eggs in other birds' nests, is governed by familiarity with her territory: although in choosing the nests she shows a preference for those belonging to particular species of song-birds, she will still, if need be, lay eggs in any unfamiliar nest (as many observers have reported) rather than go outside the bounds of her territory.

The common ownership of a territory by a mating pair increases the mutual value of both birds for each other. In the roaming phases one bird will recognise and seek out his or her mate in their territory. Here as often, preservation of the species and enhancement of individuality go hand in hand.

An inner attachment to this place develops, it becomes a 'home' associated with special values and feelings of familiarity and safety. Home is a place where through peace and security essential moods of every higher animal find most satisfaction. M. Holzapfel has shown the importance of such a home for a crater-spider: if it has caught a fly in its web, its 'appetite for home' is greater than its appetite for the prey, and it does not start sucking the fly's blood till it reaches the 'soothing' atmosphere of its favourite haunt. We have seen earlier how 'home-like' are sand-wasps' sleeping places. All these examples point to the deliberate satisfaction of a drive, which fosters a positive mood within the animal.

H. E. Howard, whom we have met so often as a pioneer in investigating bird territories, describes the bonds which link a lark to his territory: 'Watch then at the start, sometime early in February. For some days we may not see the birds, may not see any life, nor hear any song. But a morning comes when that which has long been a secret wilderness turns again into song. Mark a male as he ascends, mark the limit of his movements in air, learn his limits on the ground, and whether spiralling or wandering you will observe that he conforms to his territory below and that even when driven by the wind across his boundary he checks himself with palpable effort to beat back across it. So that he has two distinct ways of behaving with reference to his territory—air movement and ground movement. From the beginning air movement is definite and is determined by the ground plan.'

For us the open sky has associations of the utmost freedom, but for the lark—though linked with the owning of a nesting place —that sky serves to limit his freedom. Yet his jubilant singing suggests the joy of 'possession'.

Manifestations of individuality can also be seen plainly within mating pairs. All observers have noted that many of their actions, however, involve elements of aggression, often combined most strangely with attraction to the mate. Much in their behaviour can be interpreted as a fixed form of ambivalent behaviour, in which the agressive elements must be considered assertions of individuality—one of the bases for what in human life becomes the complex of selfishness.

With many animals it seems that in this reproduction season the social bond has shrunk to the duality of the pair. The territories may separate one pair widely from another, which has often been too simply seen as a sharing out of feeding space, whereas in most cases it is primarily a seasonal change in social trend typical of the species—for many birds brood without any sort of territories and yet master the problem of foraging. It need not be disputed, of course, that the trend to isolation sometimes helps tò solve that problem, as well as satisfying the individual's drive.

*   *   *

We started from a territory which isolates the brooding pairs, though they are always 'within earshot' of the rest of the flock— which is very important from a stimulation point of view. It is a big contrast between the social pressures of flock life and being just a pair, and this must mean a considerable change in the bird's inner state. But the reproduction season does not have the same effect with all birds alike: with some species general gregariousness continues even then, while with others birds are brought together in great masses by the reproduction urge itself.

Yet even in the great brooding colonies, such as those of penguins, albatrosses, terns, gulls and many other birds, the urge to mark off a small territory is manifested, and their behaviour is very similar to that just described: fierce defence of a small area round the nest, even when this nesting place is only marked by a few stones or is a flat hollow dug in the sand. The territory is small, the bird's specific 'ownership tension' subsides a few feet away from the nesting place. The colony thus shows a strange state of balance between the social and the individualist urge: it subjects the individual to the most possible social influences, but also preserves his segregation.

Although I have been talking of pairs, it is justifiable to dwell on individuality in this connection, because the male tit is the pair's leader. When I refer to the individual in the following pages, I naturally mean any complete individual of a higher animal species. But the examples tend to concern male animals, because they often express individuality more than the females do, owing to their relative freedom from the tasks of the species. Sometimes, of course, it is the other way round: apart from the actual laying of eggs, the male is sometimes more heavily committed, even exclusively so, to the social duties of brooding and rearing (as with the emu, the tinamou, and some plover species). Generally, however, the male sex is less burdened by such duties, and the male's development reveals more striking manifestations of individuality.

This is often shown very clearly in reproduction: there are many examples where the males choose, occupy and defend the territories. There are others where male and female each have their special territories, where each therefore has the best expression for his or her individuality. In the case of the stickleback (as we have seen) the male chooses the territory and defends it, builds a nest, guards the spawn, supplies them with a fresh stream of water; the female is ceremonially bowed into the nest to lay eggs and after that swims on her way. Among the cichlids too it is the male which occupies a territory.

We might indeed say that the division into two different sexual structures, which is a characteristic of all higher animal organisms, makes it possible for one of the sexes to reach the best possible expression of the species through the *unequal* distribution of reproduction duties between both. Of course it would be far too much to say the sexes were divided *for this purpose*, but because they are so divided, that possibility may be realised along with many others. Division of the sexes in the highest animal forms means increased social life in the reproduction season: increased social life makes possible the highest expression of individuality. This is a thesis which the biologist has a whole arsenal of arguments to defend.

The territory, then, is a spatial manifestation of individuality, which includes many characteristics beyond the range of the body: whether moving or at rest, the animal when awake always exists as a 'presence' exerting its influence in a wider area. Hediger (1941) refers to measurable distances representing this area, e.g. the 'safe distance' up to which the 'foreign body' is allowed to approach, and the 'critical distance' within which that body will be attacked; such distances are affected, of course, by changes in the animal's 'inner life' resulting from such factors as taming and habit.

*   *   *

In a zoo the larger animals cannot always be given sufficient space to form their own territories. Being forced nearer their neighbours than they might be if at large, they express their individuality more strikingly in other ways. The differences in their inner state, which are unmistakably shown in many patterns of behaviour, lead to social hierarchies, manifesting in very different ways the dominance of individual animals over other individuals. In the last decade, specially for birds and mammals, there has been much talk of peck orders and biting orders; and there are also hierarchies at the feeding trough, for the right to preferred places in the sun or the shade, for mating rights, and with canine species for 'superior' urinating places.

Such hierarchies doubtless play a big part in many animal societies even at large, but there are also many without them. The biologist will always have to establish how far the striking expressions of them are sometimes connected with particular living conditions, especially how far they are the result of limitations of space. In any case the animals themselves recognise their different 'degrees' and deal with each other accordingly, so the hierarchies are evidence for the force of individuality no less than is the ownership-behaviour expressed in territories.

The individual's tendency towards segregation turns other members of the species from something irrelevant, to a *Gestalt* from which stimuli go into the nervous system's controlling organs. This produces heightened vitality, which is expressed in attitude, colouring and health. The sensory effects social 'partners' have on each other will thus make for greater fulfilment, increasing both individual distinctions and mutual recognition of those distinctions. Feelings of familiarity fill the individual's environment with literally vital associations, of which he may be more or less conscious—but animal consciousness is a difficult problem.

The extension of the individual through ownership of a territory doubtless goes hand in hand with processes in consciousness of which the observer can get a glimpse through their expressions in defence and familiarity. While we recognise the mysteriousness of such processes, we must yet take them very seriously and try to come nearer the heart of the mystery. The observations of social behaviour among deer offer some possibilities in this direction, since with many species the developing of antlers has both an important social function and also produces in the individual a striking seasonal change in form and mood.

Hediger (1947) has already shown that through these antlers we may discover at least some of the traces of animal consciousness. For when an animal's ·structure can change suddenly and substantially, as with deer at the time of shedding their antlers, this must lead to observable changes in its behaviour, if it is conscious of its body. (In contrast, as Hediger points out, there are some animals, e.g. snakes and perhaps also mice, which have no consciousness of their bodies.)

I shall here confine myself to cases where the antlers are a mark of the male—leaving out of account, that is, the special situation with reindeer, where both sexes have big antlers. Year after year, in weeks of most intensive growth, the deer develops his antlers, which with red deer may make up 6% of his whole body weight. They grow from spring to mid-summer, and stay 'at their peak' throughout the winter; one day in spring they break off automatically at a preformed base under the influence of inner processes.

The deer 'knows' about his antlers, for he can take them into account in his movements. 'Deer,' says Hediger, 'are sometimes real artists in trying out all possible twists and turns which have the aim of getting through the narrow opening whereby the zoo-keeper would keep them from the hinds' enclosure.'

The antlers also have their special social value: their size and shape help to decide their owner's place in the hierarchy of the herd. It would be a mistake to try to deduce that place from the shape of the antlers alone, but this certainly plays a big part.

When it comes to fights with rivals, where the antlers have their main function, only deer with nearly the same antler strength go into action; a deer with weaker antlers does not fight but acknowledges inferiority. H. Bruhin's study (1953) of the antlers' social role yields important conclusions:—

'The position of a male with high social standing is abruptly shattered as soon as he loses his antlers. In the spring of 1951, in the Basle Zoo, I was able to watch the moment when a fallow-buck α sank to a lower level (α, β, γ, here describe the levels in social rank). On April 18th, at 3.45 p.m., the herd of five male and eight females were begging for food from the zoo visitors. Suddenly they were slightly startled by a playing child, so that some of them trotted off, including the α male. He happened to graze with the right side of his antlers the branch of a fir-tree lying in the enclosure. Immediately this half of the antlers fell clattering to the ground. Obviously upset, with tail raised, he sniffed at the piece he had just lost. Almost at the same moment the β buck realised what had happened, and attacked and pursued him vigorously. The other three yearling antler-less γ bucks took scarcely any notice of the occurrence nor did the does. After about half an hour both the α and β bucks had more or less calmed down and were again begging for food. But the former α buck was not tolerated at the fence by his rival, and therefore kept right at the back of the enclosure. There was only an indication of a social clash between α and γ bucks. Up to the evening the one-palmed animal carried out peculiar head movements, as were observed by Heck (1935) after the loss of antlers. On 23rd April the β buck also shed his first antlers. From this time on there was the same social ranking as had prevailed before the α animal shed *his*.

'In this case it can therefore be clearly established that the antlers, "representing a particular social position", also lose their significance as representative organ when one half is lost, and this loss results in its owner going down the social scale.

'In contrast to the breaking off of antler points in fights with rivals, which is irrevelant for deer, the whole antlers when normally shed continue for some time to form part of the environment of their former owner and other members of his species. In some cases, at least for a few days after the shedding, the old antlers possess for a male bearing antlers the significance of a sexual rival and are fought according to ceremonial. The symbolic effect of the antlers for social position is therefore no longer effective in connection with their former owner, but as an instrument without any function may still provoke a rival to a social clash.'

The extent to which 'something inside the deer' (to express it as cautiously as possible) 'knows' about the weapon, is shown also by the fact that the use of it begins immediately the full sweep of the antlers has been completed. (Before he has antlers the deer uses his front legs as weapon.) At this moment, if 'high-ranking' animals are at the stage of antler-shedding, they almost literally 'lose face' . . . and the favoured antler-bearer goes up in the scale for a short time. Even among red deer, where the older animals usually shed antlers before the younger, high-placed individuals are tormented after shedding; for these shifts of rank occur at a time when the younger animals' antlers are already near shedding and are therefore excluded as weapons. It is really a distinction that is 'worn'.

In an interesting example from sikas, Hediger shows (1946) that the differences of rank must rest on 'appearance' and not on any weakening of the 'bereaved' or shock effect on him: 'In this trio a socially high-ranking deer a, immediately after shedding, was vigorously and constantly chased by a very low-ranking deer γ, so that he had to be transferred to a neighbouring enclosure— where there was a β deer who had shed his antlers 23 days before and had been continually attacked at the time by the a deer. Although the a animal's shedding scars were still bloody, as soon as he got into the new enclosure, he started attacking the β animal again. So there can be no question here of a shock effect caused by the actual shedding; for a deer who has experienced a shock retires as far as possible and never spontaneously attacks, especially not on strange ground. Moreover, the sika has very small antlers compared to that of the red deer or reindeer, where one could more easily imagine a shock effect. The γ deer's attacks on the a deer directly after the latter has lost his antlers can therefore be explained only by his having thereby lost his social position as well.'

The effect on the herd of respect for the antlers—and the corresponding effect on its owner's behaviour—may be illustrated by what happened with a herd of fallow-deer in a private zoo, as reported by Bruhin: 'During rutting (December, 1952) the six-year old α buck (Albino) had to be put away, since he had forked to death a brocket (two-year-old) and a cow. He was therefore shot in the sight of the other animals. The shooting caused a distinct relaxation of tension in the herd, and the position was soon taken over by a four-year-old β buck, who had regularly fought with the α buck. The head was taken off the dead animal, and after being stuffed was kept some days in a nearby shed out of sight of the herd. Then it was fixed outside the fence of the enclosure at the level of a head poised for battle, the antlers being stuck through the mesh of the fence. As soon as the herd saw the head again, they fled as far as the enclosure allowed. But soon afterwards they cautiously approached the place, with the new leading buck going in front. He patrolled up and down at a distance of two yards from the head, eyeing it from the side. Finally he faced it and tried to fight with it. But when there was no counter-attack, he very soon gave up the "battle", and after trying a second time never again took up a battle position. The rest of the males and females in the herd were now allowed up to the head. They approached it nervously, at a distance of 1½ feet at the nearest.

'Horse-chestnuts, their favourite food, were now placed in front of the hung-up head, inside the enclosure, at various distances. All the animals ventured up to within a yard or two of the head to get the chestnuts, but only the new α deer went nearer. So in this case it could be observed that an authoritative effect, calling for distance to be kept, still emanated from the symbol of α deer (head with antlers).

'The head was then removed for a few hours and hung up again on the same day. The herd's behaviour was about the same, except that this time the young leading buck dared to sniff at the antler ends of his former rival. But he made no further attempt to fight it.'

*   *   *

The deer's antlers are a particularly striking case of an

individual animal being marked out, and of the unity of appearance and behaviour. Similar examples of such unity are to be found among many groups of higher animals. Extensive similarities in the behaviour of fishes, birds and mammals point to general basic features in the relations of the individual to the group. But there is a danger in the finding of general rules, which brings such satisfaction and is so very helpful in mastering the wealth of experience around us, that very often the no less important differences remain unnoticed. It will therefore be a good thing to notice here the differences which occur between externally similar forms in two high groups of warm-blooded animals, birds and mammals.

With both these, as with other vertebrates, the clashes between members of a species may often have the character of ceremonial duels (to which I shall be returning). But if we compare the violence of these battles, it will be noticed that with mammals, however different the duelling rules may be, the clashes are generally fiercer and more dangerous than with birds. Bruhin gives some striking examples for mammals.

'The rutting battles are often fought with such ferocity that deaths are not excluded. Not only through the infliction of severe injuries, e.g. piercing of the skull with an antler point, but both rivals may be killed in a sort of "in-fighting", i.e. the violent hooking and wedging of antlers into each other, which in most cases causes the death of both animals from exhaustion and starvation.

'As these examples show, a violent interlocking of antlers is only possible with a more highly developed type of antlers. According to Seton the finding of dead elks is something so ordinary that he believes 1 % of the male animals may be taken as dying in this way. He also suggests that this percentage may be still higher with the Virginia deer (*Odocoileus americanus*) on account of its strongly ramified antlers. The interlocking of antlers by deer with forked or brocket antlers is practically impossible. In this respect the simple antlers are therefore superior to the more complex ones, since such accidents in fights between rivals are excluded.

'With all deer species where the male has functioning antlers, the duelling ceremonial is much the same. The male does not charge at his rival furiously, as a ram does, but rather cautiously feels with his antlers for the adversary's, and the decisive thrust does not take place till the last moment. The forelegs are then more or less straddled while he levers himself forward with his rear legs. The line of the forehead runs nearly parallel with the ground. According to statistical investigations of the American zoo director Hornaday, tame deer with their antlers cause far more accidents in captivity than do lions and tigers, presumably because people do not realise that the deer's slow approach is an attack to be taken seriously—and only realise it when the animal is already attacking.

'The duelling rules for moufflon (wild mountain sheep— *Ovis musimon*) are similar to those for maned sheep, except that by their frontal attack the rivals try to push each other to one side. As soon as one achieves this, he rams his adversary from the side, often succeeding in smashing the atlas (uppermost cervical vertebra, supporting the skull). This way of fighting I was able to observe several times at the end of September 1949 in the Vincennes Zoo (Paris). I also saw peculiar behaviour on the part of two full-grown ewes, who during the rams' battle went into "battle mood", fighting each other according to exactly the same rules.'

'The example of the musk-ox (*Ovibos moschatus*) shows us forcibly that weapons which are definitely for use against enemies (from other species) may in some circumstances be used against rivals: in one case, as soon as the signal for battle was given, both bulls moved about fifty paces away from each other in great haste, and then, when the right distance was reached, dashed at each other as on a given signal. When they met in a furious charge and their powerful front skulls took the impact, it was as if two rocks were crashing against each other. Neither tottered on his legs . . . I now obtained the explanation for a bull skeleton I had found a few days before. It had a split forehead, and none of us could understand how this might have happened.' (Rasmussen, 1938.)

'The battle ceremonial of the impala antelope (*Aepyceros melampus*) is about the same as that of the kob: both rivals stand with straddled forelegs and try to stay with their heads dead opposite each other till one of them succeeds in surprising the other in a charge. The battle is sometimes so violent that one buck may literally gore his rival. On one occasion, the violent strain and shock, as the two vigorous beasts bounded together, broke off the horn, leaving the broken part, ten inches long, embedded in the other buck's chest, about three inches of the point being fixed firmly in the body, while the rest stuck out like a picket pin. Yet the buck seemed well and strong.' (Roosevelt, 1910.)

Hediger (1952) gives an impressive picture of hippopotami fighting:—

'The huge, constantly growing canine teeth of the hippopotamus are typical social equipment, used for fighting between rivals. A duel of this sort is usually decided after a fixed ceremonial. Each opponent stands more or less parallel to its rival, but facing opposite ways. Then each tries to drive its eye tooth into its opponent's flank by a powerful side stroke of the head. Cases have been known of the huge canine tooth being thrust into the heart of the defeated rival, and fragments of eye teeth are often to be found on the hippos' fighting ground.'

The analysis of these behaviour differences between birds and mammals is still in its early stages, and the scientifically usable material on mammals is far behind what has already been assembled on birds. My remarks can therefore simply point to a side of the problem which I believe deserves attention: namely, that the violence of the fights between rivals, expressing the power of a mood, is also evidence of increased individuality—a heightened 'self'.

*   *   *

This brings us to an important aspect of social biology. Behaviour research has discovered many exciting general facts which apply over widely different animal groups and levels. That insects, crabs, fishes, birds and mammals may all have territories, that there are social hierarchies (like pecking orders) in societies of very different types, that courting ceremonies are known among spiders as well as among vertebrates, submissive behaviour among fishes as well as warm-blooded creatures—all this has tended to concentrate attention on general laws of similarities, at the expense of the no less general laws of difference. So we must try to see more clearly what are the variants in the above behaviour laws, which will correspond to the varying levels of differentiation.

Peters (1950) stressed these differences, and his observations are all the more important because he also succeeded in establishing very general family types of social life extending beyond group boundaries, i.e. genuine types of social structure. He also brought out the higher degree of individualisation shown by bird families compared with those of fishes.

The jump in differentiation level is a particularly big one between cold- and warm-blooded animals. For with the keeping of an even body temperature, the individual becomes exposed to more dangers, has greater requirements for his maintenance, but is also more independent of the physical environment. While we are thinking mainly of vertebrates, we should remember that the highest social forms of insects achieve a considerable regulation of body temperature through the dispositions of their colony life—a fascinating chapter of insect sociology. The increase in differentiation in mammals and birds is obvious; with it grows the drive towards integration into society, and also the wealth of relationships with which this enforced social life enriches and enhances the individual's life.

It is characteristic of the higher vertebrates that they can respond simultaneously to drives which on a lower level are mutually exclusive in one and the same phase of life. This causes an extraordinary enrichment of the social world, as I shall try to illustrate in more detail by the mother-family. Everywhere this obtains among birds, there are thoroughly isolated family communities. Individuals which live gregariously except in the reproduction season—such as female ruffs and many gallinaceous (game) birds—when it is time for brooding and rearing young, will cut themselves off from other members of their species and only rejoin them later. There are also mother-families in isolation among mammals, e.g. some predators. We also find parent-families in isolation among mammals, even among primates, e.g. the gibbon. But the mothers and young of some mammals remain in the group—which is a new characteristic—one example being the howling apes.

'These inhabitants of Central and South America live in small hordes made up of several males and rather more females. The society's unity is shown, for instance, in the sharing of their virgin forest habitat, in which one horde will roam round nomadically, defending itself against neighbouring hordes. The mothers stay close to their young for a long time, not only feeding them but carrying them around and sometimes, when they have become more or less independent, helping them over difficult country. The males have no personal ties with the progeny. The sexes mingle at random. It can be seen from this example that the mother-families, which among lower vertebrates are quite inde-pendent, may among mammals be completely integrated into a larger group; and also that the mammals' physical organism makes new social relations possible. For it is the carrying of offspring in the mother's body which allows her to stay in the group. With birds the possession of eggs and their protection is enough to tie the birds to a particular place and cause thorough-going isolation from group life.' (Peters, 1950.)

As an example from bird life of individuals' special attachment to each other, I shall once more quote from R. A. Hinde (1952) on tits, which are highly evolved song-birds; it will be remembered that in their winter flocks the tit couples do not simply disappear as couples, but remain in special contact with each other.

'Colquhoun (1942) and Martin (1938) have described a pre-roosting ceremony between members of the pair of blue tit which takes place occasionally in the winter and more frequently as the nesting season approaches. This was seen fairly often, especially in February and March. The two birds flew together from twig to twig, sometimes with raised crest and moth-like flight, calling "Drrrrt-t-t", "Durreeee", or singing. Occasionally the two birds of the pair flew in stages up to the top of the roosting tree together, and then spirally down again to the base. Sometimes they merely sat a foot or two apart before going to roost. Occasionally the male inspected the female's roosting hole after she had entered. In the great tit the members of the pair often associated particularly closely just before roosting, and the male often accompanied the female some way towards her own roosting hole . . .

'Some weeks before the start of nest-building the male great tits start to roost in the foliage, but the females continue to roost in holes. These holes sometimes, but not always become their nesting places.

'A watch was kept on one nest of a great tit on a number of mornings and evenings after the beginning of nest-building. In the evening the male accompanied the female to the box, the female usually entering immediately. The male then sat or hopped about a few feet from the box, preening or feeding. After a few minutes, he inspected the hole of the box, clinging outside for a few seconds and then hopping up into the tree again. This was repeated several times, the male usually increasing his distance from the box between each inspection, so that he sometimes returned from 20 yards for the final one. . . . During the first stages of nest-building the male usually inspected the hole about five times after the female had gone to roost, but this behaviour became less marked during the following fortnight, and he was not seen actually to inspect the hole after the beginning of incubation.

'In the early morning, the male normally arrived at the box about half an hour before sunrise. Sometimes he started to sing immediately he arrived, sometimes he sat in silence near the box for a few minutes first. The first few notes of the song were usually thin and breathy, but they quickly gained strength.

Different variants of the song were used, the male changing from one to the other without apparent cause. . . . On some mornings he waited thus for over 40 minutes. When the female emerged, the male usually attempted to copulate immediately. . . . Once incubation had started the male became much less interested in the box, but continued to sing in the vicinity until the female came out.'

Let us remember these peaceful every-day scenes from family life alongside those of fights between rivals. For here we see specially strong ties between individuals which know each other and by staying together manifest their own particular individuality most clearly. The bond with a partner of his own species, and the 'possession' of a site, increase the bird's individuality and bring all the rich potentialities of relationship from mere potentialities to complete realisation.

10
Rituals

IN DESCRIBING PARTICULAR social relations, I have throughout this book used words like 'ceremonial' and 'ritual'; indeed, one can hardly avoid using them. The ending of disputes over territory by a submission ceremony, the use of dance movements to start courtship, the 'standardised' way in which chicks beg for food—time and again we have seen a necessary act in an animal's life strangely transformed into a particular structure of behaviour which is uniformly carried out. We also saw that such acts, even when without obvious relevance to the function they serve, are understood by social 'partners' as a sort of language. It really seems as if the partner who is thus understood has been doing 'the done thing'.

These ceremonials are carried out not only by vertebrates, in whom we are more inclined to expect behaviour akin to our own. Even among insects, whose organisation is so remote from ours, we find examples like the bee 'language' (dances), the mating of dragonflies, etc.; and we shall now look at them in a fly-group, the empids, in which the sexes find each other partly through such customs.

With the genus *Hilara* it can be observed that the male flies make strange little webs from a silk-like substance. They carry these along with them between their legs, and use them to render defenceless the smaller insects which form their food. 'With one species of this genus, the Alpine *Hilara sartor*, the veil-like, elliptical web is never used to overcome prey, but serves the males exclusively as rudder and sail in the dance-flights which they perform together in swarms. Such dance-flights have a quite definite "lane": they move first diagonally downwards from a point, then make a sharp bend to fly horizontally, and finally climb upwards in several slight curves, to a resting point, from which the whole thing begins again. The middle and rear feet carry the web dragging behind, and besides its aerostatic function this may help to give its carrier increased visibility through its opalescent sheen.' (Meisenheimer.)

This ceremonial is particularly complicated with the genus *Empis*, described by O. M. Reuter (1913):—'It is peculiar that—according to observations so far—the females do not suck any prey, except during the short time of copulation. But it is still more peculiar that the prey is always caught by the male and handed over to the female. Many careful observations by Howlett in relation to *Empis borealis* have fully confirmed this singular behaviour. The females dance up and down in the air, whereupon the males appear one by one, each holding between his rear legs a still intact insect he has caught. Every male at once chooses a female, begins copulating with her and flies with her to a nearby branch, where the mating act is completed. The female has now taken over the prey, which she kneads and sucks dry, while it is gripped partly by her own rearmost legs and partly by those of the male. Hamm later made similar observations for other empid flies.

'Aldrich and Turley have observed in North America that the males of an *Empis* species found there (*E. politea*), when hovering in the air, were generally attached to a balloon twice as large as themselves. This consisted of a layer of small concentric bubbles; according to the observers it was produced by the secretion of various glands at the posterior end of their bodies. The observers saw these males, equipped with balloons, approach the females waiting on blossoms, and they presumed that it was the balloon's function to attract the females' attention. But they also found that the balloon usually contained a captured fly, so that very probably, as with the other empids, this was given to the female as a meal. Aldrich and Turley report, however, that the balloon always sank as soon as copulation had taken place (Figure 25.)

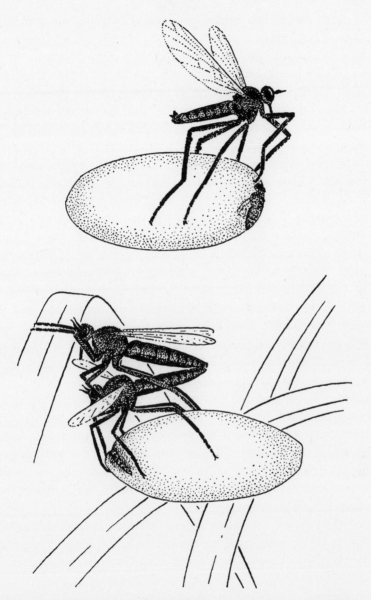

FIG. 25. The males of the fly genus *Empis* as a prelude to reproduction
carry with them a silken balloon, which usually contains a captured fly
(after Aldrich and Turley).

Shall we call this behaviour a rite? Of course any term bor-
rowed from human activity may be so narrowly limited that it can
apply only to our human sphere. But there seems no advantage in
this, and it is only a matter of convention whether we do thus limit
it, or whether we use the term as part of social life generally.

If we take the latter usage, then a 'rite' may be defined as any
co-ordinated performance of actions, fixed for a particular social
group, which is understood by the group's members. That such
ritual performances and their understanding by animals are
practically always innate, is in this connection irrelevant. If confined to human activities, on the other hand, a rite would be the
performance of social actions, fixed by tradition, which individual
members of a society must learn to carry out. As we are here
trying to examine the whole social field, I prefer to use 'rite' in its
wider sense, believing that it will help to show significant correspondences. It does not matter if we leave out of account for the
moment the different origin of ritual actions in animals and in
men. The human individual's drive towards learning and the
role of tradition in preserving our society are both involved in
almost all aspects of human existence, not only in social rituals.
Moreover, the learning of actions which form part of ritual behaviour is not confined to human beings: the specific song of
many birds, for instance, which is central to their ritual, is with
many species only learnt in the social unit. A study by Armstrong reveals an amazingly wide range of similarities between our
human dances and those of birds:—'It is not surprising that many
human dances imitate such bird-dances: in the West those of the
crane and the black grouse, those of the cassowary in New Guinea
and the emu in Australia; among Mexican Indians the spring
dances of the turkeys, among the Jivaros in the Amazon area the
dances of the orange-coloured rock-manakins—and many others.'

*   *   *

Research into ritual behaviour among animals has brought
many unexpected results and shattered many common supposi-
tions, perhaps most of all in the field of combative behaviour,

which has for so long been wrongly and one-sidedly assessed.
The Darwinian doctrine of 'the survival of the fittest' has been so
uncritically applied, even by scientists, that the combative and
destructive aspects of evolution have been over-emphasised at the
expense of those of mutual help and of ways of behaviour which
limit or avoid destructive struggle.

The most important developments of recent research concern
struggles between members of the same animal species. Those

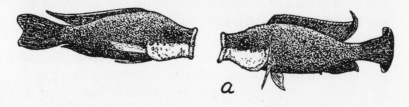

FIG. 26. Meeting of rivals in *Tilapia natalensis*. Both wear full breeding dress:
black with white throat, making contrast of colours. (a) Frontal threatening
position at borders of territory; (b) Mouth fight. Such contests usually end
without a decision, but sometimes produce slight shifts of territory (after
Baerends and Baerends-van Roon).

between different species are a quite different phenomenon, being
struggles more between hunted and prey. Hunting is primarily a
necessary, purposive part of self-preservation, and so discussion of
human combativeness is less concerned with hunting than with
the urges which in extreme cases are satisfied through murder and
war: even Man, that is, has such struggles within the species.
Research on animal behaviour, showing that the struggles are
reduced by at least temporary parting of the adversaries, is
already throwing new light on these situations in human society.

We have noticed earlier that animal aggressiveness is some-times markedly different according to the season, so that at one time life is great shoals, swarms, flocks, etc., is possible, while at reproduction times such animals are less able to 'tolerate' each other and thus seek isolation in territories. This isolation of brooding pairs, as we have seen with various fishes and know particularly well with birds, does not only help to preserve the species by distributing foraging space among its members. It also creates the peace essential for rearing (by preventing too many battles and clashes), while not completely breaking off the contact with members of the species which is so important for higher animals. Moreover when these clashes occur, they are conducted—through innate forms of behaviour—according to definite rules, which stop a futile destruction of members of the species.

The territories produce a strong effect on the individuals, an increase in vitality, as we know from our own feelings of fami-liarity and ownership. A stickleback's fighting strength, for instance, 'depends by no means wholly on its physical abilities, but on its relationship to the home and conditions there. The more precious the home it is defending, the more spiritedly it fights and the greater its prospects of victory. (This applies to many other species of animal besides the stickleback.) The case of the stickleback has been thoroughly investigated, and the following basic 'odds' can be given: (1) the male who has settled into his nest longer overcomes the newer settler; (2) a male with a nest overcomes one without; (3) one who looks after his nest well overcomes one who looks after it badly; (4) the owner of a nest with eggs overcomes the owner of a nest without eggs.' (Fischel, 1947.)

If the forming of territories restrains aggressive tendencies through a spatial order, they are also restrained by the recognition of social hierarchies like the peck order. The observer is amazed time and again at how swiftly and surely submission behaviour will stop a struggle which is threatening to blow up. This is especially striking with fishes, where (as mentioned earlier) change of colour is the conspicuous sign of submission, making even more effective the change in fin position and general attitude. The example of the leather fish (*Monacanthus ciliatus*) in the West Indies shows how the whole head-position can reinforce the expression of this mood-change—and this also plays an important part with sticklebacks. (Figures 26, 27, 28, 29.)

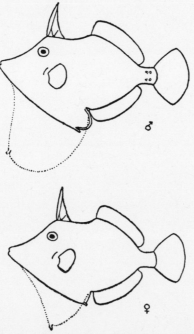

Fig. 27. The leather-fish (*Monacanthus ciliatus*), at home in West Indian waters, like all its relatives has a strong dorsal spine which can be raised, and the male's ventral sac can expand a good deal more than the female's, as is shown by dotted lines (after E. Clark).

G. Kitzler (1941) describes the battle of the lizards in the spring, and this is a real 'exhibition bout' with rules. As soon as two mature males meet, the 'act' is introduced by a threatening position. The sides have a big part in this, and we see clearly that the distribution of the lively patterns and bright colours—apart from the markings of the head—always bring the sides into

FIG. 28. Three phases of encounter between two male leather fish, the dominating one on right. We notice the changing position of the dorsal spine and tail-fin, the increasing expansion of the ventral sac, which remains in the stronger fish, but disappears with the weaker. With the stronger's 'head-stand' the eye remains in normal position, and is therefore turned. During this demonstration the colouring becomes livelier, especially on the right: the ventral sac gleams a golden yellow, enhanced by the black edging (after E. Clark).

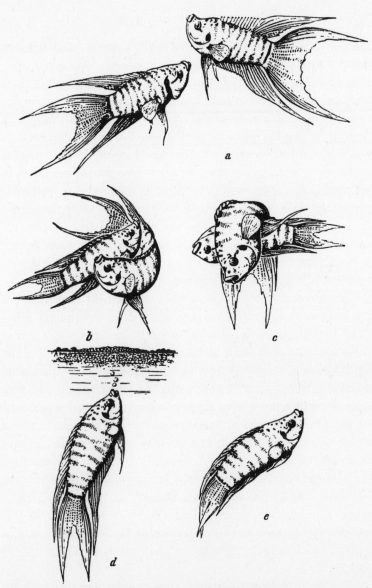

FIG. 29. From the social life of the paradise fish (*Macropodus opercularis*). (a) The male on the left with spread gill-covers threatens the fish on the right, which also adopts threatening position (with fins spread wide). (b and c) Phases of mating. (d) The male builds a mud-nest from single air-bubbles. (e) The submissive position contrasts sharply with that of the threat position (after Peters).

prominence. The lizards make themselves narrow and tall, the heads stiffen and are bent slightly downwards. An attack then follows on the back of the head, seldom anywhere else; but these bites are never very dangerous, and are generally 'taken' in the original stiff position. Now the attacker lets go, and the picture changes, in that the one who has been passive now makes his bite, which the former attacker simply lets happen. It is a sort of exchange of bites, which goes on for a little while. It is hard to see what causes a decision in the fight. Sometimes it corresponds to common expectation, with the weaker male leaving the battle-field; but at other times it is the 'last biter' who does so, possibly impressed by the firmness of his adversary stiffly standing his ground. Of course the innately fixed 'rules' do not work out with all animals in this rather idyllic way.

In the mammal world, as we have seen, a fight between rivals can be fierce enough. The weapons which defend the animal effectively against enemies of another species, sometimes play a part in these fights between rivals of the same species. But even then the fights are almost always conducted according to a ceremonial which is innately fixed for the species. In fact I hope it will now be clear that the restraint of aggressive behaviour is often achieved by innate dispositions of social relationships, a restraint which means that the positive side of aggressiveness is preserved, always expressing the peak of vitality in any animal, while at the same time the fighting 'code' stops the species losing ablebodied individuals.

Illustrating such a restraining influence, the 'prelude to a battle scene' may be highly ritualised with many refinements, and also indicate social rank, as is brought out by R. Schenkel's study of wolves, which I shall follow below (see Figures 10, 11 and 12, 30 and 31).

The stronger wolf adopts a threatening position, in which his tail is raised and quivering, his legs are stiff and may also quiver, and the hair on his back bristles. As for his face, the eyes have a rigid stare, the ears are pricked and turned a bit outwards, but the menace is conveyed above all by the impressive baring of fangs.

The whole expression suggests there will be an explosion at any moment. Together with this, high-ranking wolves will give continuous growls, varying slightly in timbre. Low-ranking wolves never growl on these occasions, but may give a short shrill yelp of fear when suddenly attacked by a stronger wolf against whom they dare not make any defence.

A slightly weaker wolf arches his back and inclines his head backwards, his tail is bent underneath with its root raised, the ears are laid back and the gaze is unsteady. A much weaker wolf shows none of the threat signs, except for baring his fangs: he

FIG. 30. Meeting of wolves of different social rank: low-ranking wolf is inhibited (ear position) by the gaze of higher-ranking animal (after R. Schenkel).

bends his legs, crouches, bends the root of his tail downwards— drawing it in; the hair on his back does not bristle, nor does he growl. In short, he shrinks instead of expanding, and the threat-position is replaced by a defence-position. The less the wolf can face a situation and so becomes defensive instead of threatening, the more quickly and more often the readiness position on both sides is followed by the actual explosion—in the movement of biting.

Real biting never occurs, except in very great battle excitement, and then only on the part of the wolf with the initiative. An

empty snapping movement is much commoner, which often
signifies rage, though it is always partly defensive. When the
wolf growls and his hair bristles, the snapping is chiefly of rage, he
barks fiercely and comes very near the adversary's body, showing
his confidence. When the snapping is purely defensive, as with a

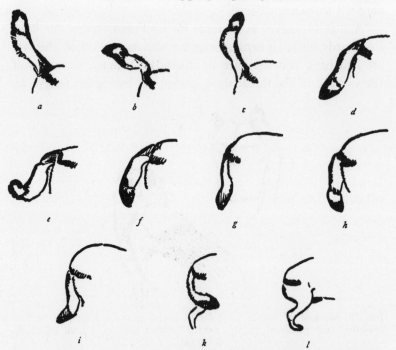

FIG. 31. Wolf's tail as organ of expression. (a) Self-confidence on meeting
other wolves. (b) Confident threat. (c) Threatening attitude with wag to side.
(d) Normal position (without social tension). (e) Not quite so confident threat.
(f) Normal position, common while wolf is eating or watching. (g) Depressed
mood. (h) Between threat and defence. (i) Active submission (wagging to side).
(k and l) Strong inhibition (after R. Schenkel, 1947).

much weaker wolf, he does not bark, and instead his jaws clap
loudly together.

In special circumstances, particularly to overrule weaker
wolves (who need not be vanquished former rivals), high-ranking
wolves may assume a position of readiness to leap, which sometimes suggests an ambush, and is even followed by a surprise

attack. But this attitude is just as often adopted quite openly as
a genuine threat, and quite obviously terrifies low-ranking wolves;
then too the high-ranker may follow up his threat with an actual
leap.

Sometimes, of course, real fights will occur, but in the main
wolves are inhibited from fighting by the ritualised performance of
these threatening gestures and movements, and are limited to such
deformed preparations for battle. This is a phenomenon widespread among vertebrates.

*   *   *

Who would have thought, looking at a lively shoal of minnows in the sun-filled water, that these small fish develop a complex system of social relations in the group, with a very striking
expression of clashes? M. Holzapfel has followed these activities
in detail:—'The same fish can be the superior when kept with a
smaller minnow and the inferior when kept with a bigger one.
This size rule can be broken, however, since social position is
decided by qualities not only physical but also psychological, such
as aggressiveness or excessive timidity. Social superiority is
expressed in pursuing other minnows. The tactics of attack are
characteristic of the minnow. The attacking fish tries to get his
head under the other fish's thorax and push him up to the surface.
In pursuit the attacker changes colour characteristically: melano-
phores (containing pigment) spread on his sides, which give them
vertical zebra stripes, a colouring I have never seen except in connection with social clashes. The pursued fish remains uniformly
light-coloured if he is completely inferior, and flees at once before
the attacker. If he offers resistance, i.e. also tries to push his
adversary upwards from the belly side, then he too shows the
striped pattern.'

To illustrate how widespread such 'battle-codes' are (of course
among highly differentiated animals), we may take a last look at
the life of the fiddler crabs, again as described by Miss Jocelyn
Crane:—

The conclusions of most other observers was verified that,

although brief duels, in which the large chelae are interlocked, are frequent, injury is exceedingly rare. I have only once seen a disablement actually take place, and this was the extreme tip of a dactyl . . .

'A definite duelling ritual was followed in all except cases of extreme provocation. . . . Usually, however, a duel proceeded as follows:—only infrequently was a duel preceded by display—i.e. by a rhythmic series of beckonings—and then never by vigorous display such as was used in courting the female. Instead the combatants first prance towards each other, stiff-legged, patting

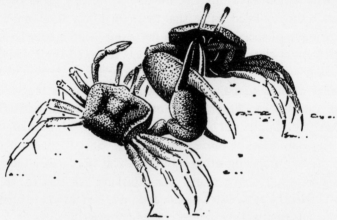

FIG. 32. Fighting male fiddler crabs (*Uca*) (after Pearse).

the ground with the bottom of the great palms and claws, as though in challenge. Then both lunge and feint a few times, with the back and sides of the semi-flexed chelipeds, which meet in audible clicks. At last after several of half a dozen such parries they proceed to the last step and interlock claws. This last movement is always undertaken warily since there is always danger that the nipper may be damaged or wrenched off. Then the claws locked, the crabs lunge in turn, pushing each other back and forth, first one and then the other sinking down and back until his shell often actually touched the ground. Usually this continues until the weaker breaks away and runs for his hole, occasionally he is

4

4

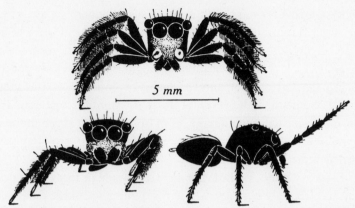

Fɪɢ. 33. Threatening and courting positions of·a South American saltigrade spider (*Corythalia xanthopa*). Above: Threat position. Only the first pair of legs touches the ground; the others increase the spider's size. Below: Courting, phase A (left), sideways swinging of body; phase B (right), stretching and raising of first pair of legs (after J. Crane).

Fɪɢ. 34. Courting positions of three South American saltigrade spiders. Above, left: *Corythalia chalcea*. If the third pair of legs is moved below the horizontal, the position means 'threat'. Above, right: *Mago dentichelis*; left and right first leg raised alternately. Below: *Ashtabula furcillata*. The first pair of legs is specialised, not used for walking, and is the only pair which is black. The posterior quarters are moved sideways during courting (after J. Crane).

somersaulted backward with a flip of his opponent's claw, often the larger simply stops fighting and moves off without there being a decision. Most duels last only a few seconds, the record was 25 minutes. . . . The provocation for a fight is usually either poaching on the territory of another male, or courting of the same female. Sometimes, however, there is no stimulus apparent for the most spirited encounters; until some better explanation is found, this must be left to sheer excess energy . . . or may simply be termed sport.' (Figure 32.)

Figures 33 and 34 show the male saltigrade (a form of spider) with its strikingly big eyes, whose threatening attitudes, duels and courting display are ritualised to an unusual extent. Primitive types of saltigrade respond to chemical stimuli, but with more evolved ones the optical stimulus is decisive (Figures 33 and 34).

*   *   *

Rituals accompanying and facilitating the business of reproduction are found in immense profusion among birds at every stage of the cycle. When they pluck leaves, blades of grass, twigs and other potential nest material, it may look like a meaningless activity, yet it has been adopted by many birds as specific behaviour, integrated especially into the preliminaries to mating, and also the ceremony of 'relieving a mate': various nest material is collected and laid before the brooding bird as a present; without this special way of approach the mate, familiar as it may be, cannot as a rule get the brooding bird to leave the eggs.

F. Goethe (1937) has described the curious behaviour he observed in a big brooding colony of herring-gulls on a flat North Sea beach:—

'A gull pair is standing at its pitch. Suddenly a neighbouring male runs up to them looking very excited, his head pulled in and held very stiff, stops from a foot and a half to several yards away from them, and pecks in the ground or the grass, keeping his beak always turned to the pair. He begins energetically tearing up blades or plant stalks, which he mostly drops again, but sometimes

Plate 29. With the Antarctic Adélie penguins the older chicks form close groups, in which they are protected all together by many old birds. But the parents still recognize their young even at this age.

Photo: Dr. J. Sapin-Jaloustre, French Polar Expeditions.

Plate 30. The female lyre-bird has not got the ornamental 'lyre'. In her whole appearance she is like a hen pheasant, but the ornithologist will recognize in the head her relationship to the song-birds.

Photo: Illustrated London News.

Plate 31. On one of his singing and dancing clearings the male lyre-bird begins his ritual.   *Photo:* Illustrated London News.

Plate 32. The male lyre-bird at the climax of his singing and dancing ritual, when he turns into a wonderful 'ornament', dominated by the great double bow of the lyre-feathers.

Photo: Illustrated London News.

throws behind him in the direction of his pitch or of the female
standing at his rear. The other male, challenged to do the same,
also dashes up to the intruder in a equally stiff attitude, stops two
or three feet away from him, and begins pecking in the grass and
tearing up stalks in the same way. Often each of them will tug at
a plant for a long time with beak stuck right out. Sometimes the
male who is "attacked" has very little "plucking urge", so that
after a brief instinctive response he stops, and does not even
resume although challenged by his neighbour again and again,
sometimes for hours on end. But if both birds are in the same
mood, the plucking becomes a frenzied business. They approach
each other, and if one stops plucking, the other quickly tries to
come still nearer him. . . . In most cases no serious fight develops
from the plucking.'

Strangely enough, no clear result of the plucking contests can
be observed. Goethe expressly states that the distribution of
territory and pitches does not change. The challenger has always
come too near his neighbour's pitch, it is true, so the latter thereupon defends it. But after the contest, when one of the two has
eventually given up and gone away, everything is unchanged.
Probably the significance of this peculiar performance lies in the
impression it makes on each of the watching females, who sees her
male giving exhibitions of strength, which increases her sense of
attachment to such a 'doughty fighter'.

Originally the plucking movement was part of nest-building.
At the reproduction season grasses and plant stalks of all kinds
have a strong attraction for gulls, who instinctively pluck them to
deposit them at the nesting-place. Herring-gulls' nests and building materials, however, are so variable that the plucking instinct,
however important as a fighting gesture, can play no essential
part in nest-building. According to Goethe, 'as well as lux-
uriously lined nests, there are also those where the eggs are on
bare sand with only a wreath of twigs and stalks round them.'
The gulls' plucking contest, therefore, offers a fine example
of an instinct's function being transformed, so that the instinct

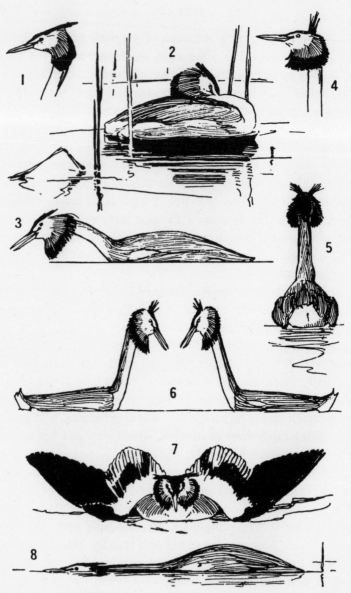

FIG. 35. The observations of the mating play of the crested grebe (*Podiceps cristatus*) by Huxley were of pioneering importance for the study of animal rituals. Our pictures show how the mates' appearance is altered by typical attitudes, supported by bristling or sleeking of feather structures. (1, 2) rest phases; (3) seeking attitude; (4–6 and 11) 'shake attitude'; (7) cat-position

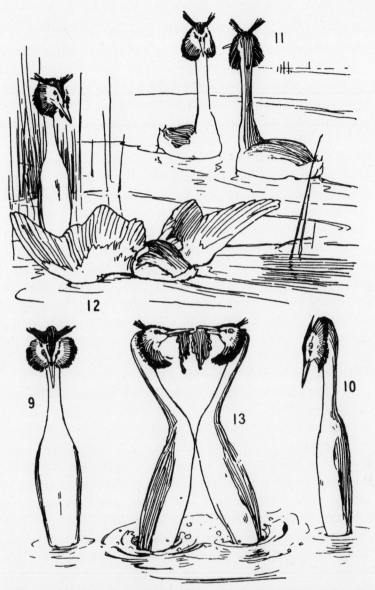

(may be adopted by both sexes); head as optical centre; (8) passive mating attitude; (9, 10 and 12) the male dives and appears in 'ghost attitude' (in 12 the female adopts the cat position); (13) the 'penguin dance': coming up from the water, lifting and touching the mate, also presenting water-plants in beak. The attitude of 13 lasts a few seconds (after Huxley, 1914).

progressively loses its original significance and serves mainly as a means of expressing strength before other members of the species.

*   *   *

Among the simple movements which in particular cases seem to have become part of a ritual is 'yawning' or gaping, by birds and mammals, which does not fit into any one set of elementary functions. As we have seen, the gaping of the young song-bird, which makes it and the old bird into a limited supra-individual unity, is an innate movement concerned with feeding which is strongly developed at an early stage of the young bird's growth. When it becomes independent, able to leave the nest, it loses also the instrument of its dependence, its beak swelling withers completely, and the throat colour pales to the usual light flesh colour of the oral cavity. But with other types of bird growing up is accompanied by a decisive transformation. Only now does the oral cavity show very bright colours: dazzling yellow with the cormorant, yellow and red with. auks, gleaming orange with a species of African shrike and with kittiwakes, bright red with the red-breasted merganser, bluey-pink with the great tern, deep black with the gannet—with both sexes in most of these cases.

It is not yet clear whether the equally bright colours of the oral cavity shown by the adult male paradise bird are an extension of the way it is coloured in the young bird or a later development on reaching sexual maturity. Whereas the colours mentioned above, apart from black, mostly belong to the yellow-red end of the spectrum, with the beautiful paradise-bird the colours are in the section of the spectrum from light yellow to bright green, apart from one species, the 'rifle-bird', which shows a blaze of white. The blue end, as far as we can say today, is very little represented, though pink and lilac are to be found. The dazzling green and yellow tints are brought to their highest effect when shown during the reproduction season in ritual yawning in front of the females (Plate 19).

The throat colours, then, are adapted to particular ways of behaviour *in adult birds*, which yawn ceremonially in particular situations. The oral cavity has its special possibilities: the closed beak conceals the surprise of an unexpected colouring. When it comes to surprises, as Armstrong says, how could they be better revealed than by a signal colour hidden in the throat?

Selous (1927) describes the yellow in the cormorant's beak as an 'oral lantern' which flares up. But the 'flaring' occurs in different connection from species to species: sometimes as threat, to keep off enemies or other members of the species, as with the African shrike (reptiles as well often show this threatening yawn). The male raven's yawn puts rival males to flight or exasperates them, but attracts female ravens. Ceremonial yawning plays a big part in the love-play of cormorants and gannets, showing the yellow or black colour (respectively) for a longer or shorter time. The movement in itself does not fit into any necessary elementary function, but may be part of a system giving an outlet for unused nervous energy. In the new situation it is as meaningless as human yawning, but a receiving structure is built into the nervous system which is 'plugged in' to the transmission 'yawning with bright throat colour'. This plugging in produces a meaningful association in these birds' life, to which there is a clear response: the yawn has become an effective signal.

Although (in contrast to human rituals) animal rituals are almost always innate patterns of behaviour, there are traces of learnt rituals among animals too, e.g. bird-song. While some song-birds, such as the reed-bunting and the tree-pipit, have the whole of their song innate to them, even if they have never heard another bunting or pipit sing, the linnet learns its song only through social contact. Sometimes a basic structure is innate but is completely developed only through living with other members of the species. The chaffinch's mating call and the very short 'rain call' of the mated males are innate, but the finch's song with its complicated end part is innate only in a vague form. If a young finch is kept isolated, the following spring it will produce only a shortened and little differentiated song. But if in its first spring it is given the chance of hearing other finches sing, it will learn the full finch song. Without this chance it will never learn, but will remain a permanent beginner (Poulsen, 1951). It is still in doubt whether this extra learning of song may be 'imprinted' in a moment or anyhow a very short time.

We should not, of course, see such phenomena as the first faint beginnings of human learning, for they are only particular 'acquired' parts fitted into limited and innate co-ordination. Even so they must be taken seriously, as a reminder that animal behaviour is not all that rigid and mechanical.

*   *   *

Comparisons of human behaviour with that of the higher animals have long been bedevilled by conflicting views about evolution. Those concerned to show the animal origins of all things human have concentrated exclusively on parts of the complex structure where such origins are to be seen; their opponents have tended to ignore everything which did not bring out the uniqueness of Man. Without taking up any position as to 'origins', I would state unreservedly that there are important similarities between the ritual behaviour of human beings and animals.

Ritual behaviour diverts the course of drives into a set of co-ordinated actions: this contributes to group preservation. Even human rituals, where particular drives are allowed free play, serve to restrain these drives in every-day life. Ritual is always social, a feature of the organisation of all higher forms of life which mould the individual from his first beginnings as part of a larger whole.

Among the drives common to human beings and animals are aggressive and gregarious tendencies, the drives towards reproduction and looking after young. The various conflicts which arise through their occurring side by side are restrained in ritual forms which give these conflicting drives play within sharply defined limits and thus help to balance them out. We have seen striking instances of this in the territorial distribution of brooding and courting space: gregarious tendencies are satisfied by having

other members of the species within sight and hearing, but ownership of a territory increases individualism and the mood of
rivalry, while at the same time limiting the aggression resulting
therefrom.

That similar restraints are at work among men is shown by
the whole history of society's structure, by the owning of property,
and by the praise of moderation as a primary virtue in all ages.
Of course there are greater variations in human behaviour owing
to Man's freedom, and human drives are therefore not so regularly
restrained by ritual as is the case with higher animals; but this is
a different aspect of the problem.

Another important similarity is the use of symbolic actions.
Childish patterns of behaviour are often to be found in sexual
ritual: e.g. in many bird species the young bird's humble begging,
with wing quivering and slightly drooping, has been incorporated
into their mating rites as part of the female's ceremonial. Movements and attitudes which have been co-ordinated from earliest
childhood have now become adapted to new nervous and
hormonal activities. The same applies to food and feeding as
symbolic in animal rituals. Common terns arrive in their brooding territory unmated and mating is proceeded by courting play in
which the male (presumably, for the sexes look exactly alike) will
offer the female a small fish. Sometimes, carrying the fish in his
bill, he will fly around with a mate in a special 'fish-flight', and the
fish is never eaten but is used on many such flights. With other
species the same 'fish-play' occurs instead in the actual sexual
ceremonies. This is the case with sandwich terns, where unions
are formed for years, perhaps sometimes for life, so that the birds
arrive in the territory already in pairs.

Both with animals and men, rituals induce particular moods,
in which unconscious impulses are given free play; the temporary
damping down of rational thought is clearly a big feature of
human rituals, and this is achieved by the extensive use of sensory
effects from music, colours, lights, scents, movements, etc.

But probably the most important similarity characterising all these ritual processes in men and animals is the suppression (or 'sublimation') of dangerous, destructive rivalries and aggression, through organised actions which 'lighten the load' of aggressiveness and distract the individual away from it. With some groups of animals such an arrangement is an essential factor in preserving the species, with men in preserving the social unit.

*   *   *

Let us now look at the differences between human and animal ritual. First of all, the way each is passed on corresponds to the whole structure of human and animal life: animal ritual is in essentials innate, like the physical marks and dress which so often play a big part in it; human ritual is in essentials acquired by learning and is passed on to succeeding generations in the form of tradition. In consequence, as with other features of human civilisation, such ritual is always liable to gradual or sudden change through the special roles of consciousness and freedom of decision, which make our form of life unique.

The rituals of higher animals fit the individual, in mood and function, into the life of the species, causing actions to be performed which have meaning only in this supra-individual whole. With Man, however, the greater whole, which such rituals serve to express, must include consciousness of past and future, knowledge and also feelings about the universe of which our own existence is only a part, and awareness too of death: hence religious rites, those concerning death and the dead, ceremonies of ancestor worship. These are indeed extensions of ritual which are unique to Man, and in which it has its finest flowering; but that need not stop us seeing its far commoner function in all social life, human as well as animal.

On the other hand, by bringing out the similarities between human and animal ritual behaviour, I am far from implying that such behaviour in Man is something primitive, a relic of the animal in us, 'the mark of the beast'. It may be a harnessing or restraining of primitive urges, for good or ill, but new rituals can be very consciously developed, for instance by governments or dictators seeking to control people's minds—as we have tragically witnessed in recent decades. Some ritual is anyhow essential for social life.

Another important difference between human beings and animals which concerns the place of ritual, is that as the former are capable of reproduction all the year round, there is nothing equivalent to the different rutting times of animals which might keep different races from inter-breeding. Human history is a ceaseless process of race-mixture, and one of the main factors which unites people of the same race, and (despite the possibility of interbreeding) divides those of different races, is the existence of different rituals—different languages are a notable example— which are largely fixed by tradition and consciously passed on for coming generations to learn.

Humanity's present problems arise partly from the coincidence of two fateful circumstances. On the one hand populations have expanded to such an extent in the last century that they have almost literally 'covered the earth', and have thus come into contact with societies which before were more or less isolated and could live their own lives; the penetration of such societies has been increased, of course, by technical progress, which is leading more and more to mass units of association. On the other hand, the formerly isolated societies were attuned, both naturally and by tradition, to an existence in small groups highly differentiated in physique, language and behaviour. The need for such an existence is basic to human nature, and is in striking contrast to the historic situation of a humanity filling the earth with different groups everywhere in frequent or continuous contract.

The tensions produced by this contrast can be resolved partly by developing new rituals, which will satisfy both the basic demand for life in small societies and also the meeting with members of the wider whole. One reason, for instance, why modern wars have become more and more 'inhuman' is that, in the old phrase, 'chivalry is dead'. *There* was a form of ritual behaviour which once limited even the fiercest battles. It needs an immense creative act to build new rituals which will extend above and across all nations. And since Man is not only a rational creature, such rituals must take into account the constant presence of irrational forces, finding a place for religious experience and all aspects of true social life. In the last resort ritual can be a mighty instrument for bringing about the brotherhood of Man.

11

The Lyre-Bird

OUR VISIT TO the dragonflies in the first chapter raised some of the basic questions concerning social life among animals. For a last look at the phenomena which help to show the animal as a social being, I shall take another particular genus, that of *Menura*, the Australian lyre-bird (Plates 30, 31 and 32, Figures 36 and 37) for which zoologists have distinguished many species very similar to each other.

They are shy birds, about the size of pheasants, inhabiting the woody mountain gorges of New South Wales, Queensland and Victoria. They prefer to keep on or near the ground, living mostly on insects and their larvae, which they find in rotten wood. They fly little, and then chiefly to some tree look-out, from which they can at any time glide off into the thickets, their real habitat.

Like many other birds we have met, their social structure is 'territorial', paradoxical as it may sound to call an isolating arrangement social. But the isolation is not accidental or caused by lack of contacts; on the contrary the lyre-bird has a great many contacts with other members of the species, meeting them in the wood, often seeing them, and keeping in touch with them through song. A small part of his large habitat, the territory, has a very particular value: it belongs to this one bird, who defends it, and has favourite spots within it which are associated with various moods, whether of peace or of great activity. These moods are an integral part of the bird's experience, and are social inasmuch as they depend on the presence of other lyre-birds in the wider area.

Both male and female have a territory of their own. This is again like a magnetic field in having the highest tension at the centre, gradually reduced the further you are from that centre.

Rivals of the same sex are driven out if they approach it, but three male lyre-birds, for instance, will meet quite peacefully at the borders of their respective territories Both sexes stick to the same territory for years; only those just becoming sexually mature must sometimes 'emigrate' in search of a new place in the woods.

The females choose their own territory, centred on the nest, which they build near some water like a 'bower', with an opening only at one side. If undisturbed, they often (perhaps mostly)

FIG. 36. Female and male lyre-bird with normal tail position.

keep to one nesting-place, but each year build a completely new nest in the old place. The male selected as mate sings in the vicinity, and from her nest the female can sometimes see several of the clearings he uses as his 'stage'.

A great deal about their life as a pair is still mysterious, but it is established that their attachment lasts for years, sometimes for life, despite the fact that the female alone carries out the tasks of nest-building, brooding and rearing. Because of this fact she often has to interrupt her brooding for foraging expeditions, so the one egg she lays may take very different times to hatch—between 35 and 50 days for birds at large. In 1940 John E. Ward succeeded in removing an egg on the day it was laid and having it hatched by a domestic hen brooding all the time. This produced a 'normal' hatching time of 28 days. The young bird is reared on the same principle as with all passerines: it 'gapes' for food, and after being fed does an about-turn, to release its droppings. These are embedded in a gelatinous covering formed by the colon only at this age. As with other passerines, the mother waits for the chick to turn, when she at once collects and removes the droppings.

The nest, then, is always immaculate, which is essential for the chick's development, since only a completely clean nest has the felt-like structure which can keep the chick warm during this first period of its life. That there is a stream flowing near the nest is no accident. The mother bird needs not only a drinking place and somewhere for an evening bathe; one of the many creeks is her 'lavatory' for the chick's droppings, which are like white pellets. They are always carried to the same place; up to 21 of them have been counted at one such spot (Thomson, 1934). A shower of rain flushes the 'lavatory' clean from time to time. As the mother has to be away foraging for long periods, she feeds the chick only a few times a day, and its colon accordingly stores the droppings for a considerable time, so that when the pellets come out, they are as long as 2 inches. If the colon is not working properly, so that the pellets are not completely formed, the mother cannot take them away. The nest becomes an evil-smelling sewer, which usually means the end of the chick.

The lyre-bird's reproduction season is from May to September (the winter of the southern hemisphere). The chicks seem to grow slowly compared to other passerines. Those of previous years stay with the mother till they are sexually mature, so she is often found with several young—L. H. Smith mentions up to 6. Chicks were generally thought to reach maturity in their fourth year, but on the basis of extensive study Smith has found that male lyre-birds' full dress is not developed till the seventh or eighth year, and that they do not always mate even then. The lyre-bird Timothy, who has become celebrated in Smith's writings and photographs, is supposed to have reached an age of nearly 25.

Many facts connected with its physical structure point to the lyre-bird being an early, archaic form of passerine; but we cannot necessarily assume that the mother-family was therefore the original family organisation for birds. There is, however, some support for this belief in the fact that the exceptional reptiles which look after their young at all (or their eggs in the case of pythons and a few others) do exhibit some sort of mother-family in its simplest form; and biologists are agreed that birds have evolved from reptiles.

Kendeigh (1952) came to the conclusion after detailed study that the parents-family (with joint care of the young) was the original form for birds. He found it more logical and probable that the father-family and mother-family should have evolved from this than the other way round. But why should not all three have developed independently of each other and parallel? I myself would think that the lyre-bird's mother-family may indeed be an early bird form, though this does not of course make the lyre-bird primitive—any more than you would call the human hand primitive just because with its five fingers it is nearer to the archaic structure of land mammals than to the forefoot of a horse or antelope. The wonderful thing is how far and how finely a primitive form has been developed, and in the case of the lyre-bird how highly specialised is the position of the *male* bird in this mother-family.

*   *   *

For although the male lyre-bird has such a small part in the actual cares and responsibilities of family life, the more observers report about him, the more important his part appears in the 'emotional' life of the family group as a whole, with the very particular activities that are demanded of him and which he carries out with such devotion.

In the area of wood which he defends as his territory (roughly a square of 200 yards) he makes a good many small 'clearings'— up to twenty have been counted for some birds—scraping leaves and earth together into a small platform, the surface of which he keeps completely clear, not tolerating a single bit of leaf or twig on them. He sometimes uses a fallen tree-trunk leaning over a stream, and on this or one of his other platforms he sings and dances as on a stage. Mrs. Edith Wilkinson, whose house is situated on the wooded slopes of Mount Dandenong, about twenty miles from Melbourne, has brought fame to the bird James, with whom she struck up a friendship after he had decided to use the wide balustrade of her veranda as a platform for his singing and dancing. He had used as much as seven places in her garden at a time for these performances, but the veranda was clearly his favourite. One small incident which took place on this veranda shows the importance of the platforms to the male lyre-bird, and also the extremely circumscribed rules which govern his daily life.

One day Mrs. Wilkinson collected a lot of juicy insects and larvae and put them on the balustrade, confident that by providing this favourite food she was giving James a splendid treat. When he arrived on the veranda, he was first of all startled, bristling his feathers in excitement, and then with an angry cry began a completely unexpected 'deck-clearing'. In five seconds he had kicked away all the insects and larvae, without eating a single one; then he flew away. A week later his hostess repeated the experiment, and this time his bout of cleaning was even more violent; indeed he stayed away from the veranda for several days.

To Mrs. Wilkinson such behaviour suggested mainly that by bringing material gifts she had marred a friendship which was strictly 'disinterested'. But I think we should rather see it as evidence of a bird's 'single-mindedness' when in a particular mood, and the way certain things in his environment will have a different meaning for him when in that mood. When he feels hungry, he does not sing or dance, but forages in the parts of his territory which he knows and trusts as good places for food. When he feels like singing and dancing, he has no interest at all in food or feeding places; the platforms are all that count, and they must be completely uncluttered. It must have upset James badly to find his dais turned into a dining-room: like any temperamental performer, he felt thoroughly 'put off'. Our human moods, of course, are both much more complex and usually much more controlled in their expression; James was here expressing mood in its simplest, clearest form.

The lyre-bird's clearings in the thicket are often only a few yards away from each other, and if he is in the mood, he will go from one to another to dance and sing and spread his feathers. On a single afternoon he has been seen at eight places one after the other, giving his 'show' over and over again, with its 'appeal' for both eye and ear.

Which bird is capable of the finest and most varied song? Even the greatest experts might give different answers, but from all reports the male lyre-bird must be in the top class, if variety of repertoire and range of sounds are among the most important criteria. He sings all the year around except for about three months, beginning in September or October, when he is moulting. From observations on birds in captivity it would seem that when they are a year old they can already perform their speciality, which is to mix their own beautiful lyre-bird song with all kinds of 'foreign' sounds, the calls of other birds and animals, and sounds from their human environment. Whether their own song is innate or acquired by experience we cannot yet say for certain, but all observers agree that the wide range of imitation is almost unique, and that hardly any sound seems to be outside it. Dogs' barking, cats' miaowing, saws' whirring, are as convincingly imitated as a flock of parrots in flight or the cheep of 'gaping' chicks; car-horns, pneumatic drills and the like, and almost in the same breath, the finest, softest twittering of small humming-birds. One morning when James was giving a recital before several guests on Mrs. Wilkinson's veranda, one of the ornithologists

present identified the song of twenty birds which he knew himself
and reported that there were several more calls he did not know—
all that in a recital lasting 43 minutes. Incidentally, James is
reported to have extended his repertoire every year with new
'numbers'.

The male lyre-bird is at his most exuberant from May to July,
but in June and July he does rather less imitations and produces
more continuously the long soft courting song of the species.
Evidently females are also skilful in imitating sounds, but do not
do it as much as the males.

This imitation is astonishing in so many respects. First of all
there is the basis for it, the fact that an organ of balance has been
transformed into one of hearing, plus the fact that sound can be
formed through the respiratory channels. Both together give the
species a very wide range of new possibilities for communication
and perception, and thus for relations to environment. Human
speech, after all, is an extreme consequence of such dispositions.

That a bird forms sounds typical of the species, produced by
innate dispositions, and that these sounds are heard and recognised
in their special quality as part of the life of the species—all this is
full of unsolved mysteries. But that such a bird is also capable of
imitating sounds, including complicated melodies, brings one up
against an even greater mystery, that of animal consciousness.

The lyre-bird hears a succession of notes or a noise which does
not come from his own species. That he eventually mimics it
shows that he once consciously heard it with full 'perception'.
But he even succeeds, through the special structure of his nervous
system, in directing his vocal organs so that they produce sounds,
the sequence of which cannot be ensured by innate co-ordination.
By a completely mysterious impulse, which follows his act of perception, groups of nerves and muscles work together unconsciously to reproduce what he has heard and go on doing so
repeatedly. The reproduction of sounds foreign to the species
must extend immensely the male bird's experience of his environment, and however reserved we try to be about the inner side of

animal experience, it seems undeniable that sounds are produced here which show no innate co-ordination; that the bird has heard and reproduced them despite their foreign structure; that they have an effect on other lyre-birds and other creatures capable of hearing.

Biology today is no longer inclined to present a dull mechanical picture of animal life, beside which even the poorest idea of humanity would appear to advantage. On the contrary, a knowledge of the complexity of animal behaviour and experience, and its similarities with human behaviour, makes it easier to see the uniqueness of Man. In this case, for instance, while recognising how far removed any animal imitation of sounds is from the least articulate human speech, we realise all that is involved in the mysterious complex of such animal imitation, which makes human speech seem *a fortiori* even more remarkable.

The lyre-bird's song is an essential means of group life. The males hear each other, and it is to be presumed that mimics of such brilliance are also an attentive audience for their fellows. In case this needed proof, we should find it in the fact that sometimes duets occur, two males singing either in unison or in harmony with each other. Even when 'imitations' are being sung, another bird may join in, sometimes pausing and listening to 'come in' at the right moment.

Observers stress that the males in their singing places always sing alone, except at times with other males on the borders of their respective territories, but not (as has sometimes been suggested) before watching and listening females. The females keep at a distance, but they may often see their mates' platforms direct from their nests, and we can assume that the singing fulfils a function in the lyre-bird's family life, not merely as constant sign of the mate's presence, but as releaser of hormonal processes, as constant stimulator of the moods the females need for carrying on their brooding and rearing business. The male's production of sounds, then, must certainly have a wide functional importance in the life of this essentially 'social' bird.

*   *   *

Only the male lyre-bird really has a right to his name, which the bird is given in all languages and which comes from the male's splendid tail-spread. As a matter of fact, the name has encouraged an erroneous conception of his characteristics, which till

Fig. 37. The male's 16 tail-feathers are specialised: 2 are fine threads with few side-branches, 12 form soft veil-feathers, and there are the 2 big lyre-feathers. The whole display apparatus is spread by strong feather muscles.

recently occurred even in zoological works: the two biggest tail-feathers, when standing straight up, form a wonderful lyre, with the softer serial feathers appearing as its strings. The photographic documentation of the last twenty years is slowly replacing the romantic idea of the lyre-bird as a showpiece of natural history by the much stranger and more surprising reality (Figure 37 and Plates 30, 31 and 32).

When at rest the male carries his tail flat like a pheasant. During ordinary daily tasks also, such as clearing out his playgrounds, the tail-feathers are only slightly raised, and he sings quietly while at this business. Courting play, however, is accompanied by a complete transformation. On his clear playground he thrusts out all his ornamental feathers with a jerk, spreading the two biggest, the 'lyre feathers', to a flat, taut bow, while the soft ones in between are thrown forward over his head like a veil. The typical bird form has vanished: corresponding to the now dominant mood of courting play, he is completely transformed—into a flat ornament, a 'quivering surface of spread feathers'. Turning in a semi-circle, he almost seems to lose balance as he makes a show of scratching and looking for food. Turning in that semi-circle again and again, shaking his feathers hard, he gets up on his toes to his full height. Opening the fantail and closing it again, he jumps forward, then retires a bit, while producing an amazing succession of bush noises, from the whipbird to the cry of the 'laughing jackass' (kookaburra). The sunlight plays on the lower side of the great lyre-feathers, which is usually out of sight, reflecting tints from ebony to bronze and crimson (Ward).

The lyre-bird's life reaches a peak of intensity during the reproduction season, which is expressed in the remarkable combination of tunefulness and 'ornamental' appearance. How did these, and other such features, originate? Many neo-Darwinists would see them as sensory media of selection value, since the releaser effect of the whole courting display makes for preservation. Others, however, would attribute them to natural laws which cannot be explained exclusively by the selection value of chance mutations. Personally I start from the presumption, which I believe would be generally admitted, that we do not know the basic causes for the origins of animal organs, and in trying to explain them must reckon with many factors so far unknown. It is clear, however, that once the organs have been formed, they are liable to be modified by innate mutations, when they may have positive or negative selection value.

The variation of many organs of display may very well be explained within certain limits by mutations and selection, but the general form of most parts of the display, whether scent, sounds or visual organs, goes far beyond the range of the mutations known to us. I have referred earlier to the selection value of the albino peacock, which can dispense with the colour effect of the eyes in its tail-spread. In 1953 D. Magnus, experimenting with models on the mating behaviour of the mother-of-pearl butterfly (*Argynnis paphia*), has shown that as key stimulus the basic colour of the wing is alone effective as releaser, while the special marks on it have no stimulus value. 'They may be there,' he writes, 'so long as they do not encroach on the basic colour of the wing in its general effect.' Behind this 'may' there are all the hidden development factors we do not yet know of, though in course of time we may gradually be able to turn some of the 'mays' into 'musts'. I am not denying that mutational change occurs and that selection has its effect on the forms once evolved; but if we are aiming at a comprehensive picture of nature, the mutation theory offers very fragmentary insights, and it can hardly be thought that this theory will give an adequate answer to the immense problem of organic origins.

Animal structures and ways of behaviour exhibit characteristics going far beyond the needs of self-preservation, and may often be pure self-expression of the species. Display organs, with greatly heightened expression value, may also, however, take over elementary species-preserving social functions: i.e. become releasers for social ways of behaviour (though this function need not have anything to do with how they originated). On the other hand, mutations favoured by selection may very well heighten the development of organs, and so heighten their expression value as well. In the present state of our knowledge many possibilities must be left open, avoiding the choice between two mutually exclusive alternatives.

The same applies to the phenomena by which an animal's shape, colour and attitude help to conceal it from sight, and to such mysterious developments as mimicry: obviously mutation and selection value may have been at work in preserving and modifying them. It is doubtless important within limits to prove experimentally that certain types of fly are protected from predators by being like wasps, or that if animals with conspicuous colouring are uneatable, their colouring contributes to their preservation. But this in no case explains how the special characteristic of colour, shape, 'uneatability', etc., came into being.

To return to the lyre-bird, whichever part of his courting ritual we consider, the song and sound formation, the number of platforms, the way he keeps these clean and clear, or the details of his visual transformation, we always discover developments which go beyond all mere preservation functions. This applies particularly to his amazing gift for imitation, which shows how little such a directed action is limited to any releaser function. The complexities of the lyre-bird's song, in fact, establish that it is not an 'economic' principle at work, but the expression of inner states with a quite different value where economy is irrelevant.

Certainly social life plays an important part in preserving the individual and the species, and the individual also has special functions as part of a higher order, contributing to the preservation of the group. But the biologist can no longer confine himself to this one aspect; he must also examine the features in individual and species life which show how typical social structures are formed, sometimes extending over widely different groups, such as birds and fishes. He must also see that there are important contrasts as well as similarities between these structures at their various levels of differentiation, and realise the wider experience of environment and contact between individuals which become possible as the nervous system becomes increasingly complex. The question of how complex social forms developed out of simpler ones may be dealt with by evolution research, but that can be only one of many questions that need answering. A wide-ranging general morphology will bring out the important features in social life which are specific to the particular animal form and therefore play a vital part in the species' self-expression. Just as regular migration of terns from Labrador to Patagonia—there and back in a year—must rank as characteristic of the species quite outside the laws of self- or species-preservation, so the lyre-bird's clearing of platforms, his tail-spread, his extended repertoire of sounds and songs, are unique and unmistakable media of self-display.

*　　*　　*

Decades ago, when I began my zoological work, social research on animals was confined to the amazing special cases of the great insect societies, apart from a few phenomena like bird and other migrations, and scattered facts which appeared in zoological works as a 'biological appendix'. Today such facts are the centre of attention, owing to the change in emphasis of research.

It is now appreciated that the life of all higher animals is basically social, that social behaviour in its most different aspects is an essential feature of that life. Careful observation, growing more and more penetrating as its methods continually improve, has opened new vistas into animal life: movements, attitudes, gestures, sounds, scents, markings, ways of meeting, inconspicuous to the superficial glance and earlier unnoticed, are recognised as significant, playing their part in social life. Long-despised expressions of higher animal life are now in the full limelight, an encouraging sign for the next phase of biology and zoology in the field, the zoos and the laboratory. In past decades every research expedition collected new species of animals from undiscovered continents, and brought them home to the centres of Western civilisation—animal forms which are almost taken for granted by the present generation. Today it is a host of fascinating new facts which have been collected by the observations of social research, and given point and purpose: facts which before, if noticed at all, were dismissed as superficial incidentals.

But the development of social research does not only bring out new aspects in the wide panorama of higher animal life; it also helps to form a new conception of the organism. The most powerful effect must be produced by the particular quality of the animal's inner state, manifested time and again in fresh expressions: the fact that each individual is the centre of an activity which is both typical of the species and of the individual, an activity related to time and space in a particular form of experience. However strict research workers may be in accepting only the most limited factual observations, they still find that such observations testify to the existence of that living, functional centre.

If a dragonfly's wing-structure is a source of astonishment and delight for our gaze, and a fact full of unsolved problems for research, an equally astonishing fact is the dragonfly's possession of a daily territory, an integration of the surrounding space into the individual insect's experience, a space of which that insect is the centre, which in a clearly understandable way belongs to it and greatly extends its effective 'presence' beyond the bounds of the body. If we examine very thoroughly a higher animal's nervous system and sense organs, we must also penetrate into the patterns of behaviour whereby the animal makes a section of the space-time continuum into an integrated part of its life filled with significant features.

With this turn to the world of qualities and significances, biological research restores to Man a precious heritage. A heightened awareness of the outer world, such as natural science is continually producing, always conceals a danger of impoverishing the inner world. But the new social biology brings the examination of this inner world to a central place—and also leads to a new view of human society.

This new view will not, of course, supply explanations for all human activity, but will underline the uniqueness of Man, as I have said many times in this book, by giving preciser knowledge of the high differentiation level of higher animals, and full importance to the animal's inner state. For with its increasingly wide survey of externals, the new social biology strengthens also the awareness that in the colourful world of animal life we are constantly meeting something secret and hard to grasp: the animal as a social being mysteriously related to Man himself.

Sources and Select Bibliography

GENERAL

Allee, W. C., *The Social Life of Animals*, London/Toronto, 1938.

Buytendijk, F. J. J., *Traité de Psychologie animale*, Coll. Logos, Paris, 1952.

Maidl, F., *Die Lebensgewohnheiten und Instinkte der staatenbildenden Insekten*, Vienna, 1934.

Merlean-Ponty, M., *La structure du comportement*, 2nd ed., Paris, 1949.

Portmann, A., *Probleme des Lebens*, Basle, 1949.

Other books of general interest referred to in specific chapters are distinguished by an asterisk.

Chapter 1

Buchholtz, Christiane, 'Untersuchungen an der Libellen-Gattung Calopteryx-Leach unter besonderer Berücksichtigung ethologischer Fragen', *Zeitschrift f. Tierpsychol.*, Vol. 8, 1951.

Wesenberg-Lund, C., 'Odonatenstudien', *Internat. Rev. d. ges Hydrobiol. u. Hydrographie*, Vol. 6, 1913.

Moore, N. W., 'Notes on the Oviposition Behaviour of the Dragonfly *Sympetrum striolatum Charpentier*' and 'On the "so-called" Territories of Dragonflies (Odonata, Anisoptera)', *Behaviour*, Vol. IV, 1952.

Kennedy, C., 'Notes on the Life History and Ecology of the Dragonflies of Central California and Nevada', *Proc. U.S. Nat. Mus.*, Vol. 52, 1917.

Uexküll, J. von, *Umwelt und Innenwelt der Tiere*, Berlin, 1921, 2nd ed.

Altum, J. B. T., *Der Vogel und sein Leben*, Münster, 1868.

Howard, E., *Territory in Bird Life*, London, 1920.

Chapter 2

Fabre, J. H., *Souvenirs entomologiques*, Paris, 1879-1907 (Eng. trans. De Mattos, 1912).

Baerends, G. P., 'Fortpflanzungsverhalten und Orientierung der Grabwespe (*Ammophila campestris Inr.*)', *Tijdschr. f. Entomol.*, Vol. 44, 1941.

Peckham, G. W. and E. G., 'On the Instincts and Habits of the Solitary Wasps', *Wiscons. Geol. Nat. Hist.*, Surey, Bull. 2, 1898; and *Wasps, social and solitary*, Westminster, 1905.

Adriaanse, A., 'Ammophila campestris Latr. und Ammophila adriaansei Wilcke', *Behaviour*, Vol. 1, 1947.

Huxley, J. S., 'The Courtship-habits of the Great Crested Grebe (*Podiceps cristatus*)', *Proc. Zool. Soc.*, London, 1914.

Arn, H., 'Zur Biologie des Alpenseglers (*Micropus melba*)', *Schweiz. Archiv f. Ornith.*, Vol. 2, 1945.

Weitnauer, E., 'Am Neste des Mauerseglers (*Apus apus*)', *D. Ornith. Beob.*, Vol. 44, 1947.

Tinbergen, N., and Perdeck, A. C., 'On the Stimulus Situation releasing the Begging Response in the newly hatched Herring Gull Chick (*Larus argentatus*)', *Behaviour*, Vol. 3, 1950.

Goethe, F., 'Beobachtungen und Untersuchungen zur Biologie der Silbermöwe (*Larus argentatus*) auf der Vogelinsel Memmertsand', *Journ. f. Ornith.*, Vol. 85, 1937.

Hinde, R. A., 'The Behaviour of the Great Tit (*Parus major*) and some other related Species', *Behaviour*, Suppl. II, Leiden, 1952.

*Hediger, H., *Wild Animals in Captivity*, London, 1950.

Eipper, P., in *Deutsche Zeitung*, 22. July, 1953 (No. 58).

Chapter 3

*Portmann, A., *Die Tiergestalt*, Basle, 1948.

Bernard, F., 'Généralités sur la vie sociale', in Grassé, *Traité de Zool.*, Paris, Vol. 10, 1951.

*Tinbergen, N., *Social Behaviour in Animals*, London, 1953.

Grassé, P.-P., 'Termites' *Traité de Zool.*, Paris, Vol. 9, 1949, and 'L'essaimage des Termites. Essai d'analyse causale d'un complexe instinctif', *Bull. Bio. France et Belg.*, Vol. 76, 1942.

Peters, H., *Grundfragen der Tierpsychologie*, Stuttgart, 1948; and 'Zum Problem der Gemeinschaft in der Tiersoziologie, *Studium Generale*, Vol. 3, 1950.

Buytendijk, F. J. J., *Wege zum Verständnis der Tiere*, Zürich (undated).

Hediger, H., 'Biologische Gesetzmässigkeiten im Verhalten von Wirbeltieren', *Mitteil. Nat. Ges.*, Bernfor, 1940, pub. 1941; and 'Observations sur la Psychologie animale dans les Parcs Nationaux du Congo Belge'. *Explor. d. Parcs Nat. Congo Belge, Mission Hediger-Verschuren*, Part I, Brussels, 1951.

Pitman, C. R. S., *A Game Warden among his charges*, London, 1931.

Darling, F. Fraser, *A Herd of Red Deer*, Oxford, 1937.

Altman, Margaret, 'Social Behaviour of Elk, *Cervus canadensis nelsoni*, in the Jackson Hole Area of Wyoming', *Behaviour*, Vol. 4, 1952.

Kenyon, K. W., and Wilke, F., in *Journal of Mammalogy*, Vol. 34, No. 1, 1953.

Plessner, H., *Die Stufen des Organischen und der Mensch*, Berlin and Leipzig, 1928.

Carpenter, C. R., 'A Field Study of the Behaviour and Social Relations of Howling Monkeys', *Compar. Psych. Monographs*, Vol. 10, No. 2, 1934; and 'A Field Study in Siam of the Behaviour and Social Relations of the Gibbon' (*Hylobates lar*), Vol. 16, No. 5, 1940.

*Portmann, A., *Biologische Fragmente zu einer Lehre von Menschen*, 2nd ed., Basle, 1951; and *Natur und Kultur im Sozialleben*, Basle, 1945.

Chapter 4

Uexküll, J. v., and Sarris, E. G., 'Das Duftfeld des Hundes', *Zeitschr. f. Hundeforsch*, Vol. 1, 1931.

Cristoffel, H., *Trieb und Kultur, zur Sozialpsychologie, Physiologie und Psychohygiene der Harntriebhaftigkeit*, Basle, 1944.

Hediger, H., 'Die Bedeutung von Miktion und Defäkation bei Wildtieren, Schweiz'. *Zeitschr. f. Psych. u. ihre Anwendungen*, Vol. 3, 1944; 'Säugetier-Territorien und ihre Markierung', *Bijdragen tot de Dierkunde*, Vol. 28, 1949.

Frisch, K. von, 'Über einen Schreckstoff der Fischhaut und seine biologische Bedeutung', *Zeitschr. f. vergleichende Physiologie*, Vol. 29, 1941; and *Aus dem Leben der Bienen* 'Verständl. Wissenschaft', 5th ed., Heidelberg, 1953.

Thorpe, W. H., 'The Concepts of Learning and their Relation to those of Instinct', *Symposia Soc. Exp. Biol.*, No. 4, Cambridge, 1950.

Grassé, P.-P., 'Termites', in *Traité de Zool.*, Paris, Vol. 9, 1940.

Lüscher, M., 'Untersuchungen über das individuelle Wachstum bei der Termite *Kalotermes flavicollis Fabr.*', *Biol. Zentralblatt*, Vol. 71, 1952; and 'Über die Determination der Erzatzgeschlechtstiere bei der Termite *Kalotermes flavicollis Fabr.*', *Rev. Suisse de Zool.*, Vol. 58, 1951.

Roosevelt, Theodore, *African Game Trails*, 1910.

Crane, J., 'Crabs of the Genus Uca from the West Coast of Central America', *Zoologica*, New York, Vol. 26, 1941.

Chapter 5

Monakow von and Mourgue, *Biologische Einführung in das Studium der Neurologie und Psychopathologie*, 1930.

Roesch, G. A., 'Untersuchungen über die Arbeitsteilung im Bienenstaat I und II', *Zeitschr. f. vergl. Physiol.*, Vol. 2, 1925, and Vol. 12, 1930.

Oettingen-Spielberg, Therese zu, 'Über das Wesen der Suchbiene', *Zeitschr. f. vergl. Physiol.*, Vol. 31, 1949.

Shafer, G. D., *The Ways of a Mud Dauber*, Stanford University Press, California, 1949.

Craig, W., 'Appetites and aversions as constituents of instincts', *Biol. Bull.*, Vol. 34, 1918.

Lorenz, K., 'The Comparative Method in Studying Innate Behaviour Patterns', *Symposia Soc. Exper. Biol.*, No. IV, 1950.

Koehler, O., 'Die Analyse der Taxisanteile instinktartigen Verhaltens', *Symposia Soc. Exp. Biol.*, No. 4, 1950.

Hinde, R. A., 'Appetitive Behaviour, Consummatory Act and the Hierarchical Organisation of Behaviour . . .', *Behaviour*, Vol. V, 1953.

Fabricius, E., 'Zur Ethologie junger Anatiden', *Acta Zool. Fennica*, Vol. 68, 1951.

Thorpe, W. H., 'Some problems of animal learning', *Proc. Linn. Soc.*, London, Part 2, 1944.

Holzapfel, M., 'Analyse des Sperrens und Pickens in der Entwicklung des Stars', *Journ. f. Ornith*, Vol. 87, 1939.

Tinbergen, N., and Kuenen, D. J., 'Über die auslösenden und richtunggebenden Reizsituationen der Sperrbewegung von jungen Drosseln (*Turdus merula* and *T. ericetorum*)', *Zeitschr. f. Tierpsych.*, Vol. 3, 1939.

Prechtl, H. F.R., 'Zur Physiologie der angeborenen auslösenden Mechanismen, I: Quantitative Untersuchungen über die Sperrbewegung junger Singvögel', *Behaviour*, Vol. 5, 1953.

Wackernagel, H., 'Der Schnabelwulst des Stars (*Sturnus vulgaris*), ein Beitrag zur postembryonalen Entwicklung der Sperlingsvögel', *Revue Suisse de Zool.*

Chapter 6

Koller, G., 'Über Chromatophorensystem, Farbensinn und Farbwecksel bei *Crangon vulgaris*', *Zeitschr. f. vergleich. Physiol.*, Vol. 5, 1927.

Parker, G. H., *Animal Colour Changes and their Neurohumours*, Cambridge, 1948.

Cannon, W. B., *Bodily changes in Pain, Hunger, Fear and Rage*, 2nd ed., Boston, 1953.

Howard, E., *A Waterhen's Worlds*, Cambridge, 1940.

Lack, D., 'Some aspects of instinctive behaviour and display in Birds', *The Ibis*, 1941.

*Tinbergen, N., *Social Behaviour in Animals*, London, 1953.

Chapter 7

Hediger, H., 'Beiträge zur Säugetier-Soziologie', *Colloq. Internat. C.N.R.S.*, Publ. 34, Paris, 1952.

*Baerends, and Baerends-van Roon, J. M., *An Introduction to the Study of the Ethology of Cichlid Fishes*, Leiden, 1950.

Peters, H., 'Experimentelle Untersuchungen über die Brutpflege von *Haplochromis multicolor*, einem maulbrütenden Knochenfisch', *Zeitschr. f. Tierpsych.*, Vol. 1, 1937.

*Lack, D., *The Life of the Robin*, London, 1943 (4th rev. ed., 1946).

*Tinbergen, N., *The Study of Instinct*, Oxford, 1951.

Petersen, B., Törnblom, O., and Bodin, N. O., 'Verhaltensstudien am Rapsweissling and Bergweissling', *Behaviour*, Vol. IV, 1952.

Dewar, D., *Birds of the Plains*, London and New York, 1908.

Murphy. Quoted in Armstrong *Bird Display*.

Craig, W., 'Oviposition induced by the male in Pigeons', *Journ. Morph.*, Vol. 22, 1911.

Patel, M. D., 'The Physiology of the formation of Pigeons-Milk', *Physiol. Zool.*, Vol. 9, 1936.

Kaila, Spitz and Wolf: work discussed in A. Portmann, *Biologische Fragmente*.

Chapter 8

Portmann, A., 'Die werdende Menschheit, Das Ursprungsproblem der Menschheit', in *Historia Mundi*, Vol. 1, Berne/Munich, 1952.

Guénot, L., *Evolution Biologique*, Paris, 1951.

Huxley, J., *Evolution*, London, 1942, 4th ed., 1945.

Simpson, G. G., *The Meaning of Evolution*, London, 1950.

Goldschmidt, R. B., 'Evolution, as viewed by one Geneticist', *American Scientist*, Vol. 40, 1952.

Guyénot, E., 'Deux Problèmes insolubles de la Biologie transformiste', *Les Cahiers de Foi et Vérité*, Genève, 1950.

Dalcq, A. M., 'Le problème de l'Evolution est-il près d'être résolu?' *Annales Soc. Roy. Zool. Belgique*, Vol. 82, 1951.

Calverton, V. F., *The Making of Man, an Outline of Anthropology*, New York, 1931.

Sapin-Jaloustre, J., 'Découverte et description de la "Rookery" de Manchot Empereur (*Aptenodytes forsteri*) de Point Géologie (Terre Adélie)', *L'Oiseau et R.F.O.*, Vol. 22, 1952.

Chapter 9

*Hinde, R. A., *The Behaviour of the Great Tit* (Parus major) *and some other related Species*, Leiden, 1952.

Meyer-Holzapfel, Monika, *Die Bedeutung des Besitzes bei Mensch und Tier*, Biel, 1952.

Bally, G., *Vom Ursprung und von den Grenzen der Freiheit*, Basle, 1944.

Holzapfel, Monika, 'Die nicht optische Orientierung der Trichterspinne Agelena labyrinthica', *Zeitschr. f. vergl. Physiol.*, Vol. 20, 1933.

Howard and Nobel. Quoted in Armstrong *Bird Display*.

Hediger, H., 'Ist das tierliche Bewusstsein unerforschbar?' *Behaviour*, Vol. 1, 1947.

Bruhin, H., 'Zur Biologie der Stirnaufsätze bei Huftieren', *Physiologia Compar. et Oecol.*, Vol. 3, 1953.

Hediger, H., 'Zur psychologischen Bedeutung des Hirschgeweihs', *Verh. Schweiz. Nat. Ges. Zürich*, 1946.

Chapter 10

Meisenheimer, J., *Geschlecht und Geschlechter im Tierreich*, Jena, 1921, Vol. 1.

*Reuter, O. M., *Lebensgewohnheiten und Instinkte der Insekten bis zum Erwachen der sozialen Instinkte*, Berlin, 1913.

*Armstrong, E. A., *Bird Display and Behaviour*, London, 1947.

Schneirla, T. C., 'Levels in the psychological capacities of Animals' in *Philosophy for the Future*, Macmillan Comp., 1949.

Fischel, W., *Die kämpferische Auseinandersetzung in der Tierwelt*, Leipzig, 1947.

Kitzler, Gertraud, 'Die Paarungsbildung einiger Eidechsen', *Zeitschr. f. Tierpsych.*, Vol. 4, 1941.

Schenkel, R., 'Ausdrucksstudien an Wölfen', *Behaviour*, Vol. 1, 1947.

Holzapfel, Monika, 'Die soziale Rangordnung bei Elritzen', *Verh. Schweiz. Nat. Ges. Locarno*, 1940; and 'Versuche über das soziale Verhalten der Elritzen (*Phoxinus laevis*)', *Verh. Schweiz Nat. Ges. Sitten*, 1942.

Crane, J., 'Comparative Biology of Salticid Spiders at Rancho Grande, Venezuela', Part IV, 'An Analysis of Display, *Zoologica*, New York, Vol. 34, 1949.

Goethe, F. Quoted here from Fischel.

Poulsen, H., 'Inheritance and Learning in the Song of the Chaffinch, *Fringilla coelebs L.*', *Proceed. X Int. Ornith. Congress*, Uppsala, 1951.

Chapter 11

Pratt, A., *The Lore of the Lyrebird*, Melbourne, 1937.

Ward, J. E., 'In the Haunts of the Lyre Bird', *Bull. N.Y. Zool. Soc.*, Vol. 42, 1939; and 'The Passing of the Lyre Bird', Vol. 43, 1940.

Thomson, D. F., 'Some Adaptations for the Disposal of Faeces: The Hygiene of the Nest in Australian Birds', *Proceed. Zool. Society*, London, 1934, pub. 1935.

Kendeigh, S. C., *Parental Care and its Evolution in Birds*, Ill. Biol. Monographs, Vol. 22, Urbana, 1952 (Illinois).

Magnus, D., '*Bewegung* als optischer Schlüsselreiz beim Paarungsverhalten des Kaisermantels *Argynnis paphia*', *Compte Rendus Int. Zool. Congress*, Copenhagen, 1953.

Baerends, G. P., 'Specializations in Organs and Movements with a releasing Function', *Symposia Soc. Exp. Biol. IV*, Cambridge, 1950.

Köhler, W., *The Place of Value in a World of Facts*, New York/London, 1938.

Index

Index

DATE DUE

MAY 16 '86			
APR 28			
5-1-95			

591.5
P837   Portmann
       Animals as social beings

SAN FRANCISCO UNIFIED SCHOOL DISTRICT

ESEA

1967-68